Washington Square

华盛顿广场

- Henry James （美）著
- Kieran McGovern （英）改写
- 高黎 译

外语教学与研究出版社

牛津大学出版社

(京)新登字 155 号

京权图字：01-2002-6593

图书在版编目(CIP)数据

华盛顿广场/(美)詹姆斯(James, H.)著；(英)麦戈文(McGovern, K.)改写；高黎译.—北京：外语教学与研究出版社，2003.10
(书虫·牛津英汉双语读物)
ISBN 7-5600-3774-7

Ⅰ.华… Ⅱ.①詹… ②麦… ③高… Ⅲ.英语—对照读物，小说—英、汉 Ⅳ.H319.4：I

中国版本图书馆 CIP 数据核字(2003)第 096678 号

华盛顿广场

著　　(美) Henry James
改写　(英) Kieran McGovern
译　　高　黎
*　　*　　*
责任编辑：徐　婳
出版发行：外语教学与研究出版社
社　址：北京市西三环北路 19 号 (100089)
网　址：http：//www.fltrp.com
印　刷：北京新丰印刷厂
开　本：850×1092　1/32
印　张：5
版　次：2003 年 12 月第 1 版　2003 年 12 月第 1 次印刷
书　号：ISBN 7-5600-3774-7/H·1905
定　价：5.90 元
*　　*　　*
如有印刷、装订质量问题出版社负责调换
制售盗版必究 举报查实奖励 (010)68917826
版权保护办公室举报电话：(010)68917519

"书虫·牛津英汉双语读物"是外研社和牛津大学出版社联合奉献的一大阅读精品,受到了广大英语学习者的热烈欢迎,连续多年畅销不衰。为了满足读者朋友更加广泛的阅读需求,我们再次推出18本新的"书虫"系列英汉双语读物,期待与您的相约。

关于本书

在19世纪的纽约,成功的标志就是在华盛顿广场拥有一幢自己的房屋,奥斯汀·斯洛珀医生就是一个成功的人。他生活时尚,为人风趣,又聪明机智,很招人喜爱。

这些特点在他女儿凯瑟琳身上却一个也看不到。她是一个善良单纯的姑娘,热爱并崇拜自己的父亲,一心一意想讨他的欢心,却令他非常失望。斯洛珀医生从不指望凯瑟琳身上会发生什么有趣或令人激动的事情。

但是华盛顿广场的生活最终却变得很不平静。这里发生了一段罗曼史,一个相貌英俊的年轻人来到这里追求凯瑟琳。凯瑟琳的姑姑,头脑简单的彭尼曼夫人着实为此感到高兴;她觉得莫里斯·汤森非常迷人,凯瑟琳当然也是这么认为的。可是,斯洛珀医生对年轻的汤森先生却有着截然不同的看法。医生很有钱,也知道自己死后凯瑟琳会继承一笔每年3万美元的遗产。他想知道这样一个英俊潇洒的年轻人为什么会追求他那毫无趣致的女儿……

WASHINGTON SQUARE

To own a house in Washington Square is a sign of success in nineteenth-century New York, and Dr Austin Sloper is a successful man. He is also fashionable, interesting, amusing, and clever.

His daughter Catherine is none of those things. She is a good, simple girl, who loves and admires her father and always tries hard to please him, but she is a great disappointment to him. Dr Sloper does not expect any interest or excitement from Catherine.

But life in Washington Square does become rather exciting, after all. Romance arrives, in the shape of a handsome young man who comes to court Catherine. This pleases Catherine's foolish aunt, Mrs Penniman, very much; she thinks Morris Townsend is charming, and so of course does Catherine. Dr Sloper, however, looks at young Mr Townsend rather differently. The Doctor is a rich man, and is conscious that after his death Catherine will inherit a fortune of 30,000 dollars a year. He wonders why such a charming and handsome young man is courting his dull daughter ...

Contents
目　　录

1
Poor Catherine

In the first half of the nineteenth century there lived in New York a very successful doctor. His success was for two reasons. He was, without doubt, a good doctor, intelligent and honest, but he also knew how to please his patients. He gave long, careful explanations about the illness, and always gave them some medicine to take. Indeed, his patients were fond of saying that they had the best doctor in the country.

By the time he was fifty, Doctor Austin Sloper was quite a famous person in New York. His conversation was clever and amusing, and no fashionable party in the city was complete without him.

He was also lucky. In 1820, at the age of twenty-seven, he had married, for love, a very charming girl, who had a fortune of ten thousand dollars a year. For about five years Doctor Sloper was a very happy husband; he continued to work as a doctor and each year became more experienced and more successful.

Some of the experience, however, was very unwelcome. His first child, a little boy of great promise, died at three years of age. Neither the mother's love nor the father's medicine could save him. Two years later Mrs Sloper had a second child, a little girl. This disappointed the Doctor,

1. 可怜的凯瑟琳

19世纪上半叶,纽约住着一位事业很成功的医生。他成功的秘诀有两条。毫无疑问,他是一个德才兼备的好医生,此外他还知道怎样令病人满意。他对病人所患的疾病总是不厌其烦地详加解释,而且也总是给他们开些药。真的,他的病人都喜欢说给他们看病的是国内最棒的医生。

到50岁的时候,奥斯汀·斯洛珀医生已经是纽约响当当的人物了。他谈吐机智风趣,城里上流社会的聚会从来都少不了他。

他运气也好。1820年他27岁的时候,他为了爱情娶了一位很迷人的姑娘,姑娘每年有1万美元的进项。有五年左右的时间,斯洛珀医生是一个非常幸福的丈夫;他继续行医,经验越来越丰富,事业也越来越发达。

但有些经历却很不愉快。他的头一个孩子,一个前途光明的小男孩儿,三岁的时候不幸夭折了。母亲的爱和父亲的药都没能救活他。两年后斯洛珀夫人生了第二个孩子,是一个小女孩儿。这让医生很失望,他

quite a *used to indicate that a person or thing is unusual.* 异常的,出众的。**charming** *adj. delightful.* 迷人的;可爱的。**of great promise** *likely to become very good.* 大有希望的,前程远大的。

3

who had wished for another son to take the place of the first, but there was worse news to come. A week after the child was born, the young mother fell ill, and before another week had passed, she was dead.

For a man whose profession was to keep people alive, Austin Sloper had certainly done badly in his own family, but the only person who blamed Doctor Sloper was Doctor Sloper himself. He felt that he had failed, and he carried this private blame for the rest of his life.

He still had his little girl, whom he named Catherine after her poor mother. She grew up a strong and healthy child, and her father knew that he would not lose her.

When the child was about ten years old, the Doctor invited his sister, Mrs Lavinia Penniman, to stay with him. He had two sisters and both of them had married early in life. The younger one, Mrs Almond, was the wife of a rich man and the mother of a large family. Elizabeth Almond was a comfortable, reasonable woman and Doctor Sloper preferred her to his sister Lavinia. However, Lavinia's husband had died at the age of thirty-three, leaving his wife without children or fortune, and so Doctor Sloper invited his sister to stay while she looked for rooms to rent. No one really knew if Mrs Penniman ever looked for rooms, but it is certain that she never found them.

After six months the Doctor accepted the fact that his sister was never going to leave. Mrs Penniman told

本来希望再生个儿子来代替长子的位置，不过更糟的事情还在后面。孩子出生一个星期后，年轻的母亲就病倒了，才不到一个星期，她就不治而亡。

对于一个以治病救人为职业的人来说，奥斯汀·斯洛珀在自己家里确实表现得很糟，不过也只有斯洛珀医生会埋怨自己。他觉得自己很失败，而且终其一生他都这么暗暗地谴责自己。

他还有这个小女孩儿，他给她取名凯瑟琳，跟她可怜的母亲的名字一样。她逐渐长成了一个健康结实的孩子，她的父亲知道不会失去她了。

孩子 10 岁左右的时候，医生邀请他姐姐拉维尼娅·彭尼曼夫人来和他小住一段时间。他有两个姐妹，两人都很早就出嫁了。年纪轻一些的那个，也就是阿尔蒙德夫人，她丈夫是个有钱人，家里有一大群孩子。伊丽莎白·阿尔蒙德的日子过得舒心，人又明白事理，相比他姐姐拉维尼娅，斯洛珀医生更喜欢她。可是，拉维尼娅的丈夫 33 岁时就过世了，抛下她一个人，既没有孩子，也没有财产，所以斯洛珀医生邀请他姐姐和他们小住一段时间，再一边找房子租住。没人知道彭尼曼夫人有没有找过房子，但可以肯定她从未找到过。

六个月后，医生知道他姐姐永远不会离开了，也就接受了这个现实。除了对她弟

take the place of sb. /sth. *replace sb. /sth.* 代替某人或某事物。private *adj. not（to be）revealed to others；secret.* 不公开的；秘密的。

everyone except her brother that she was Catherine's teacher. Doctor Sloper guessed that this was her explanation, and he found the idea laughable since he did not think his sister was very intelligent. In fact, he did not have a good opinion of women at all. The only woman he had ever admired had been his wife.

He was always extremely polite to Lavinia, but he had no interest in her opinions or conversation. He only spoke to her to inform her of his wishes for Catherine.

Once, when the girl was about twelve years old, he said to his sister, 'Try to make a clever woman out of her, Lavinia. I should like her to be a clever woman.'

Mrs Penniman looked at him. 'My dear Austin,' she said, 'do you think it is better to be clever than to be good?'

'Good for what?' asked the Doctor. 'You are good for nothing unless you are clever. Of course I wish Catherine to be good, but it will not make her a better person to be a fool.'

Mrs Penniman was a tall, thin, fair woman. She was romantic, and her brother knew that she loved little secrets and mysteries.

'When Catherine is about seventeen,' he said to himself, 'Lavinia will try and persuade her that some young man with a moustache is in love with her. It will be quite untrue. No young man, with or without a moustache, will

弟,彭尼曼夫人逢人便说她是凯瑟琳的老师。斯洛珀医生猜想她是这么向别人解释的,他感到这种想法很可笑,因为他从来都没觉得他姐姐有多聪明。实际上,他对女人根本没什么好感。他惟一崇拜过的女人就是他妻子。

他对拉维尼娅总是彬彬有礼,但对她的想法或她说的话却毫无兴趣。只有在想要告诉她他对凯瑟琳的期望时,他才会跟她说话。

小女孩儿大约 12 岁的时候,有一次,他对姐姐说:"想办法让她变得聪明点儿,拉维尼娅,我希望她成为一个聪明的女人。"

彭尼曼夫人看着他。"我亲爱的奥斯汀,"她说,"你觉得聪明比善良更重要吗?"

"善良有什么用?"医生问道,"人要是不聪明就一点儿用都没有。我当然希望凯瑟琳做个好人,可是当个傻瓜并不会让她成为更好的人。"

彭尼曼夫人是位个头高挑、身材瘦削、面容姣好的女人。她很浪漫,她弟弟知道她喜欢小秘密和神秘的事情。

"等到凯瑟琳 17 岁左右的时候",他自言自语道,"拉维尼娅就会想法让她相信某个长着小胡子的年轻人爱上她了。这肯定不会是真的。没有哪个男人,不管长没长小胡

have a good opinion of sb. *think well of sb.* 对某人有好感。**good for nothing** *completely useless and worthless.* 无用的。**be in love (with sb.)** *feel affection and desire (for sb.).* 热恋着(某人)。

7

ever be in love with Catherine. '

Catherine was strong and healthy, but she did not have any of her mother's beauty or her father's cleverness—in fact, there was very little that was interesting about her at all. She was large and well built, with brown hair, a round face, and small, quiet eyes. The more generous friends of Doctor Sloper noticed that she was well behaved and polite; others thought she was just dull. But Catherine was not someone people spent much time talking about.

She was extremely fond of her father and very much afraid of him. She wanted to please him more than anything in the world, but although Doctor Sloper was usually kind to Catherine, he was very disappointed in her. He wanted to be proud of his daughter, but there was nothing to be proud of in poor Catherine. She was not elegant or pretty or charming like her mother. And by the age of eighteen Mrs Penniman had still not made her a clever woman.

Over the years, however, Doctor Sloper got used to his disappointment. 'I expect nothing from her,' he said to himself. 'If she gives me a surprise, I will be happy. If she doesn't, I shall not lose anything. '

At this time it did not seem possible that Catherine would ever surprise anyone. She was always very quiet, saying so little in conversation that she seemed almost stupid. But she was silent because she was shy, uncomfortably, painfully shy. In fact, she was a very gentle, sensitive girl.

子,会爱上凯瑟琳。"

凯瑟琳健康结实,可惜她既没有继承母亲的美貌,也没有继承父亲的智慧——实际上,她身上几乎没有什么吸引人的地方。她个头大,发育得很好,长着棕色的头发,圆圆的脸和一双安静的小眼睛。斯洛珀医生那些比较宽厚的朋友们发现她举止得当,待人礼貌;别的人却认为她呆头呆脑。但凯瑟琳并不是人们乐于谈论的对象。

她极爱自己的父亲,但又很害怕他。世界上她最乐意做的事情莫过于讨父亲的欢心了,可是虽然斯洛珀医生对凯瑟琳总的来说不错,心里却对她颇感失望。他想为女儿感到自豪,但可怜的凯瑟琳身上却没有什么值得他自豪的地方。她不像她母亲那样举止优雅,美丽迷人。一直到她18岁,彭尼曼夫人也没把她培养成一个聪明的女人。

不过,随着时光的流逝,斯洛珀医生也习惯了这种失望。"我对她没什么指望,"他对自己说,"如果她能给我带来惊喜,我会高兴。如果不能,那我也没什么损失。"

到了这个时候,凯瑟琳似乎已不大可能给任何人带来惊喜了。她总是安安静静的,话很少,显得有些木讷。她不爱说话是因为害羞,这种羞怯让她感到不自在而且痛苦。实际上,她是个很温柔敏感的女孩儿。

elegant *adj. tasteful and stylish in appearance or manner.*(相貌或仪态)优雅的;文雅的;高雅的。
used to sth. /doing sth. *having learned to accept sth.; accustomed to sth.*(对某事物)已适应,已习惯。

Slowly Catherine realized that she was changing from a girl into a young lady. She began wearing expensive clothes in very bright colours—rather too bright for Doctor Sloper. When she was twenty, she bought a red and gold evening dress, and did not seem to realize that it made her look ten years older. Doctor Sloper preferred simple, elegant things, and it annoyed him to think that his child was both ugly and badly dressed, though he kept this opinion private.

It must be added that Catherine was expected to become a very rich woman. She had already inherited some money from her mother, but the Doctor had been making twenty thousand dollars a year by his profession and saving half of it. One day, this growing fortune would pass to Catherine.

In 1835 Doctor Sloper moved his family to a more fashionable address. He built himself a handsome, modern house in Washington Square, which was just around the corner from Fifth Avenue. Across the road from the house, in the centre of the square, was a pretty garden, which was open to everyone though few people ever used it.

Mrs Almond lived further out of the city in a house that was almost in the country. She had nine children, and Catherine went with Mrs Penniman to see her cousins every week. The little Almonds were now growing up; the boys had been sent off to college or to work in offices, while the girls looked for suitable husbands.

慢慢地,凯瑟琳意识到自己正从一个女孩儿变成一个年轻女子。她开始穿价格昂贵、色彩艳丽的服装——对于斯洛珀医生来说,那些颜色实在太艳了。她20岁的时候,买了一件红色和金色相间的晚装,而且好像完全没觉得这条裙子让她显得比实际年龄大了十岁。斯洛珀医生偏爱简洁雅致的东西,一想到自己的孩子长得丑,衣服穿得也难看,他就觉得生气,不过这些想法他从没表露出来。

必须提到的是,凯瑟琳可能会很有钱。她已经从母亲那里继承了一些钱财,不过医生每年行医的收入有两万美元,其中有一半都攒了下来。这笔不断增长的财富终有一天会传给凯瑟琳。

1835年,斯洛珀医生把家搬到了一个更时尚的地方。他在华盛顿广场靠近第五大道的地方为自己建了一幢气派时髦的房子。从房子里出来,穿过一条大道,走到广场的中间,就是一个漂亮的花园,花园向所有人开放,不过几乎没有人光顾。

阿尔蒙德夫人住在远离城区的一幢房子里,那里几乎是乡下了。她有九个孩子。每周凯瑟琳都会和彭尼曼夫人去看她的堂兄弟姊妹。阿尔蒙德家的孩子现在已经长大了;男孩子们要么去上大学,要么就到办公室上班,而女孩子们则在挑选合适的丈夫。

prefer *v. choose sth. rather than sth. else; like sth. better.* 宁可,更喜爱。**send sb. off** *send someone to another place.* 送走。

11

When Mrs Almond gave a party for her younger daughter Marian, who had become engaged to a promising young man, Catherine, naturally, was invited. At this time she was twenty-one years old, and Mrs Almond's party was the beginning of something very important.

阿尔蒙德夫人的小女儿玛丽安和一个很有前途的年轻人订婚了,阿尔蒙德夫人为她举办了一个订婚晚会,凯瑟琳自然在受邀之列。当时她已经 21 岁了,阿尔蒙德夫人的晚会为她揭开了一段重要的人生序幕。

engaged (to sb.) *adj.* (*of a person or two people*) *having agreed to marry.* (指一人或两人)已订婚的。

2
A handsome young man

Not long after the dancing had begun at the party, Marian Almond came up to introduce Catherine to a tall young man. She told Catherine that the young man very much wanted to meet her, and that he was a cousin of Arthur Townsend, the man she was engaged to.

Catherine always felt uncomfortable when meeting new people. The young man, Mr Morris Townsend, was very handsome, and when Marian went away, Catherine stood in front of him, not knowing what to say. But before she could get embarrassed, Mr Townsend began to talk to her with an easy smile.

'What a delightful party! What a charming house! What an interesting family! What a pretty girl your cousin is!'

Mr Townsend looked straight into Catherine's eyes. She answered nothing; she only listened, and looked at him. He went on to say many other things in the same comfortable and natural way. Catherine, though silent, was not embarrassed; it seemed right that such a handsome man should talk, and that she should simply look at him.

The music, which had been silent for a while, suddenly began again. He smiled and asked her to dance. Catherine gave no answer, she simply let him put his arm around her, and in a moment they were dancing around the room. When

2. 一个英俊的年轻人

　　晚会上的舞会开始后没多久,玛丽安·阿尔蒙德就把凯瑟琳介绍给了一位高个子年轻人。她告诉凯瑟琳这个年轻人很想见她,他是她未婚夫阿瑟·汤森的表兄。

　　凯瑟琳遇到生人的时候总是觉得不自在。这个叫莫里斯·汤森的年轻人长得很英俊,玛丽安走开后,凯瑟琳站在他面前,不知道该说些什么好。不过还没等她感到尴尬,汤森先生就已经带着轻松的笑容和她聊起天来了。

　　"这个晚会真令人高兴! 这房子真漂亮! 这一家人真有趣! 你表妹长得真美!"

　　汤森先生直视着凯瑟琳的眼睛。她什么也没说;她只是听着,并望着他。他继续以同样轻松自如的方式讲了很多其他的事情。凯瑟琳尽管很沉默,却没有感到不自在;似乎这样英俊的人就应该讲话,而她就应该只看着他。

　　音乐停了一会儿之后又突然响了起来。他微笑着请她跳舞。凯瑟琳没回答,只是任由他用胳膊搂住自己,不一会儿他们就在房

embarrassed *adj. feeling self-conscious awkward or ashamed.* 不自然的,扭捏的,尴尬的,害羞的。
easy *adj. (attrib.) not stiff or embarrassed.* (作定语)自如的;不拘束的。

15

they paused, she felt that she was red, and then, for some moments, she stopped looking at him.

'Does dancing make you dizzy?' he asked, in a kind voice.

Catherine looked up at him. 'Yes,' she murmured, though she did not know why; dancing had never made her dizzy.

'Then we will sit and talk,' said Mr Townsend. 'I will find a good place to sit.'

He found a good place—a charming place; a little sofa in a corner that seemed meant for two persons.

'*We* will talk,' the young man had said; but he still did all the talking. Catherine sat with her eyes fixed on him, smiling, and thinking him very clever. She had never seen anyone so handsome before.

He told her that he was a distant cousin of Arthur Townsend, and Arthur had brought him to introduce him to the family. In fact, he was a stranger in New York—he had not been there for many years. He had been travelling around the world, living in many strange places, and had only come back a month or two before. New York was very pleasant, but he felt lonely.

'People forget you,' he said, smiling at Catherine.

It seemed to Catherine that no one who had seen him would ever forget him, but she kept this thought to herself.

中翩翩起舞了。他们休息的时候,她感到脸都红了,后来有一段时间,她不再看他。

"跳舞让你觉得头晕吗?"他问道,声音很亲切。

凯瑟琳抬起头看着他。"是啊。"她低声说道,虽然她不知道为什么;跳舞从没让她觉得头晕过。

"那我们就坐下来说会儿话吧,"汤森先生说道,"我来找个好座位。"

他找到了一个好地方——一个很吸引人的地方;角落里有一个好像专供两人坐的小沙发。

"我们聊聊。"年轻人说;不过仍然是他一个人在说话。凯瑟琳坐在那里,目不转睛地看着他,微笑着,觉得他真聪明。她从未见过这么英俊的人。

他告诉她自己是阿瑟·汤森的远房表兄,阿瑟带他过来,把他介绍给这家人。实际上,他对纽约还很陌生——他有好多年没来过这里了。他一直在世界各地旅行,在很多陌生的地方生活过,直到一两个月前才回来。纽约是一个很快乐的地方,但他却感到孤独。

"人家都把你忘了。"他微笑着对凯瑟琳说。

凯瑟琳觉得任何见过他的人都不会忘记他,但她没有把这想法说出来。

fix one's eyes on sb./sth. *look at someone or sth. carefully.* 凝视着(某人或某物)。 **keep sth. to oneself** *not tell other people about sth.* 不把某事告诉别人。

They sat there for some time. He was very amusing, and Catherine had never heard anyone speak as well as he did—not even an actor in a theatre. And Mr Townsend was not like an actor; he seemed so sincere, so natural.

Then Marian Almond came pushing through the crowd of dancers. She gave a little cry, which made Catherine blush, when she saw the young people still together. She told Mr Townsend that her mother had been waiting for half an hour to introduce him to somebody.

'We shall meet again,' he said to Catherine, as he left her.

Her cousin took Catherine by the arm. 'And what do you think of Morris?' she asked.

'Oh, nothing particular,' Catherine answered, hiding what she really felt for the first time in her life.

'Oh, I must tell him that!' cried Marian. 'It will do him good. He's so terribly conceited.'

'Conceited?' said Catherine, staring at her cousin.

'So Arthur says, and Arthur knows about him.'

'Oh, don't tell him!' said Catherine.

'Don't tell him! I have told him that many times.'

Half an hour later Catherine saw her Aunt Penniman sitting by a window, with Morris Townsend—she already knew the name very well—standing in front of her. He was saying clever things, and Mrs Penniman was smiling.

Catherine moved away quickly; she did not want him to

他们在那里坐了一会儿。他很风趣,凯瑟琳从未听到过谁说话像他那么动听——连剧场的演员也比不上他。而且汤森先生并不像个演员;他看起来如此真诚自然。

后来玛丽安·阿尔蒙德穿过跳舞的人群走了过来。当她看见这两个年轻人仍在一起时,不由得轻轻地惊呼了一声,凯瑟琳羞得脸都红了。她告诉汤森先生她母亲想把他引见给别人,已经等他半个小时了。

"我们以后再见。"他离开的时候对凯瑟琳说道。

表妹拉着凯瑟琳的胳膊。"你觉得莫里斯怎么样?"她问道。

"哦,一般吧。"凯瑟琳回答道,没有暴露内心第一次感受到的真实情感。

"哦,我一定要把这话讲给他听!"玛丽安大声说道,"这对他有好处。他太自负了。"

"自负?"凯瑟琳盯着表妹说道。

"阿瑟是这么说的,阿瑟了解他。"

"哦,别跟他说!"凯瑟琳说。

"别跟他说! 我已经跟他说过好多回了。"

半小时之后凯瑟琳看见彭尼曼姑姑坐在窗边,莫里斯·汤森——她已经很熟悉这个名字了——站在她面前。他正在讲一些机智的话,而彭尼曼夫人则在微笑。

凯瑟琳迅速走开了;她不希望他转过身

blush *v. become red in the face (because of sth.).* (因某事物)脸红。**particular** *adj.* (*attrib.*) *more than usual, special, exceptional.* (作定语)特殊的;特别的。**conceited** *adj. full of conceit.* 极其自负的。

19

turn round and see her. But she was glad he was talking to Mrs Penniman because it seemed to keep him near to her.

In the carriage, as they drove home, Catherine was very quiet, and Doctor Sloper talked with his sister.

'Who was that young man you spent so much time with?' he asked. 'He seemed very interested in you.'

'He was not interested in me,' said Mrs Penniman. 'He talked to me about Catherine.'

'Oh, Aunt Penniman!' Catherine murmured.

'He is very handsome and very clever,' her aunt went on. 'He spoke in a—in a very charming way.'

The Doctor smiled. 'He is in love with Catherine, then?'

'Oh, father!' murmured the girl, thankful that it was dark in the carriage.

'I don't know that; but he admired her dress.'

Admiring just the dress, instead of the person, might not seem very enthusiastic, but Catherine did not think this. She was deeply pleased.

Her father looked, with a cool little smile, at her expensive red and gold dress. 'You see,' he said, 'he thinks you have eighty thousand dollars a year.'

'I don't believe he thinks of that,' said Mrs Penniman; 'he is too fine a gentleman.'

'He must be extremely fine not to think of that!'

'Well, he is!' Catherine cried, before she knew it.

看到她。但她很高兴他在和彭尼曼夫人谈话，因为这样似乎把他和她拉近了。

在回家的马车上，凯瑟琳很安静，而斯洛珀医生则在和他姐姐说话。

"和你在一起待了那么长时间的年轻人是谁啊?"他问，"他好像对你挺感兴趣的。"

"他对我不感兴趣，"彭尼曼夫人说，"他在跟我讲凯瑟琳。"

"哦，彭尼曼姑姑!"凯瑟琳低声叫道。

"他很英俊，也很聪明，"她姑姑继续说道，"他说话很——很吸引人。"

医生笑了:"那么他是爱上凯瑟琳了?"

"哦，爸爸!"女孩儿低声说道，幸好车厢里比较黑。

"我不知道;不过他夸奖她的裙子。"

夸奖她的裙子，而不是欣赏她本人，这似乎显得并不怎么热情，不过凯瑟琳不这么认为。她感到非常开心。

她父亲冷笑着看着她那条价格不菲的红色和金色相间的裙子。"你看到了，"他说道，"他以为你一年有 8 万美元的收入呢。"

"我不相信他会这么想，"彭尼曼夫人说，"他可是个挺不错的绅士。"

"他一定要顶好才不会那么想!"

"嗯，他就是!"凯瑟琳想也没想就脱口而出。

admire *v. regard sb. / sth. with respect, pleasure, satisfaction, etc.* 钦佩;赞赏;羡慕。**enthusiastic** *adj. full of enthusiasm.* 热情的;热心的。

'I thought you had gone to sleep,' her father answered. 'The hour has come!' he added to himself. 'Lavinia is going to arrange a romance for Catherine.'

A few days after Mrs Almond's party, Morris Townsend and his cousin called at Washington Square. Catherine and her aunt were sitting together by the fire in the parlour.

Arthur Townsend sat and talked to Catherine, while his companion sat next to Mrs Penniman. Catherine, usually so easy to please, tonight found Arthur rather uninteresting. She kept looking over at the other side of the room, where Morris Townsend was deep in conversation with her aunt. Every few minutes he looked over at Catherine and smiled, and she wished that she was sitting nearer to him.

Arthur seemed to notice that Catherine was interested in his companion. 'My cousin asked me to bring him,' he explained. 'He seemed to want very much to come. I told him I wanted to ask you first, but he said that Mrs Penniman had invited him.'

'We are very glad to see him,' said Catherine. She wished to talk more about him, but she did not know what to say. 'I never saw him before,' she went on.

Arthur Townsend stared. 'But he told me he talked with you for over half an hour the other night.'

'I mean before the other night. That was the first time.'

'Oh, he has been away from New York—he has been all round the world.'

"我还以为你已经睡着了。"她父亲回答道。"已经是时候了!"他自己又想,"拉维尼娅要为凯瑟琳安排一段罗曼史。"

阿尔蒙德夫人的晚会之后几天,莫里斯·汤森和他表弟一起去造访华盛顿广场。凯瑟琳和她的姑姑当时正坐在客厅的壁炉边。

阿瑟·汤森坐下来和凯瑟琳说话,而他的同伴则坐在彭尼曼夫人旁边。通常凯瑟琳是很容易被人逗乐的,可是这天晚上她却觉得阿瑟很令人厌烦。她不停地朝屋子的另一边望去,莫里斯·汤森和她姑姑正在那里谈得起劲。每隔几分钟,他就朝凯瑟琳看一眼,对她笑笑,而她希望自己坐得离他更近点儿。

阿瑟好像注意到凯瑟琳对他的同伴很感兴趣。"我表哥让我带他来,"他解释道,"他好像很想来。我告诉他我想先问问你,但他说彭尼曼夫人已经邀请他了。"

"我们很高兴见到他。"凯瑟琳说。她希望能多谈谈他,但又不知道说什么。"我以前从没见过他。"她继续说。

阿瑟·汤森瞧着她:"可他告诉我那天晚上他和你聊了半个多小时呢。"

"我的意思是那晚之前。那次是第一次。"

"哦,他一直不在纽约——他在世界各地跑。"

parlour n. (formerly) *sitting-room in a private house, esp. one where people may receive visitors or talk privately.* (旧时)起居室,客厅,会客室。**companion** n. *person or animal that goes with, or spends much time with another.* (相伴的)人或动物;同伴;伙伴。

'My aunt likes him very much,' said Catherine.

'Most people like him—he's so brilliant—though I know some people who say my cousin is too clever.'

Catherine listened with extreme interest. If Morris Townsend had a fault, it would naturally be that one, she thought. After a moment she asked, 'Now that he has come back, will he stay here always?'

'If he can find something to do,' said Arthur. 'He's looking around for some kind of employment or business, but he can't find anything.'

'I am very sorry,' said Catherine.

'Oh, he doesn't mind,' Arthur said. 'He isn't in a hurry.'

Catherine thought about this, then asked, 'Won't his father take him into his business—his office?'

'He hasn't got a father—he has only got a sister,' said Arthur Townsend. And he looked across at his cousin and began to laugh. 'Morris, we're talking about you.'

Morris Townsend paused in his conversation with Mrs Penniman, and stared, with a little smile. Then he stood up.

'I'm afraid I was not talking about you,' he said to Catherine's companion. 'Though I can't pretend that Miss Sloper's name did not enter our conversation.'

Catherine thought that this was a wonderfully clever thing to say, but she was embarrassed by it, and she also

"我姑姑很喜欢他。"凯瑟琳说。

"大多数人都喜欢他——他很聪明——虽然我也知道有些人说我表哥聪明过头了。"

凯瑟琳怀着极大的兴趣听着。如果莫里斯·汤森有什么缺点的话,那自然是这一点了,她想。过了一会儿,她问道:"那他现在回来了,他会长住在这里吗?"

"如果他能找到事做的话。"阿瑟说,"他正在四处找工作或看有没有生意可做,不过什么也没找到。"

"真遗憾。"凯瑟琳说。

"哦,他不在乎,"阿瑟说,"他不着急。"

凯瑟琳想了想,然后问道:"他父亲难道不让他一起做生意——在他的办公室里工作吗?"

"他没有父亲——只有一个姐姐。"阿瑟·汤森说。接着他朝表哥望去,笑了起来:"莫里斯,我们正在说你呐。"

莫里斯·汤森暂时中断了和彭尼曼夫人的谈话,瞧着他们,脸上带着微笑。然后他站了起来。

"恐怕我刚才可没在说你,"他对凯瑟琳的同伴说道,"但是我不能假装我们的谈话中没有提到斯洛珀小姐的名字。"

凯瑟琳认为这么说实在是太机智了,但她又为这种说法感到局促不安,所以她也站

in a hurry *eager*; *impatient*. 急切;赶紧。

25

got up. Morris Townsend stood looking at her and smiling; he put out his hand to say goodbye. He was going, and though he had not said anything to Catherine, she was still glad that she had seen him.

'I will tell her what you have said—when you go!' said Mrs Penniman with a little laugh.

Catherine blushed—she felt they were almost laughing at her. What in the world had this beautiful young man said? She saw that he was looking at her kindly.

'I have not talked with you,' he said, 'and that was what I came for. But it will be a good reason for coming another time. I am not afraid of what your aunt will say when I go.'

After the two young men had left, Catherine, who was still blushing, gave Mrs Penniman a serious look.

'What did you say you would tell me?' she asked.

Mrs Penniman smiled and nodded a little. 'It's a great secret, my dear child, but he is coming here to court you!'

Catherine was serious still. 'Is that what he told you?'

'He didn't say so exactly, but he left me to guess it. I'm good at guessing.' Mrs Penniman gave her niece a soft little kiss. 'You must be very nice to him.'

Catherine stared—she was amazed. 'I don't understand you,' she said. 'He doesn't know me.'

'Oh yes, he does. He knows you more than you think. I have told him all about you.'

了起来。莫里斯·汤森站在那里，微笑着看着她；他伸出手说再见。他要走了，虽然他一句话也没和凯瑟琳说，她仍然很高兴能见到他。

"我会告诉她你说的话——在你走之后！"彭尼曼夫人笑了一笑说道。

凯瑟琳羞红了脸——她觉得他们好像是在嘲笑她。这个漂亮的小伙子到底说了些什么呢？她发现他正和善地看着她。

"我们还没说过话，"他说，"我来就是想和你谈谈的。不过这样就有很好的理由再来了。我不担心我走后你姑姑会说些什么。"

两个年轻人离去之后，凯瑟琳的脸上仍带着红晕，她严肃地看了彭尼曼夫人一眼。

"你说要告诉我什么？"她问。

彭尼曼夫人微笑着点了点头。"这是个大秘密，我亲爱的孩子，不过他要来追求你呢！"

凯瑟琳仍然一脸严肃："他是这么跟您说的吗？"

"他没确切地这么说，不过我猜是这样。我不会猜错的。"彭尼曼夫人轻轻地吻了一下她的侄女，"你对他一定很好。"

凯瑟琳瞪大了眼睛——她感到很惊奇。"我不明白您的意思，"她说，"他并不了解我。"

"哦不，他了解的。他比你想像的更了解你。我把你的事情都跟他说了。"

court v. (dated) (of a man) try to win the affections of (a woman), with a view to marriage. (旧)(指男子)向(女子)献殷勤；向(女子)求爱或求婚。

'Oh, Aunt Penniman!' said Catherine in a frightened voice. 'He is a stranger—we don't know him.'

'My dear Catherine, you know very well that you admire him.'

'Oh, Aunt Penniman!' said Catherine again. Perhaps she did admire him—though this did not seem to her a thing to talk about. But she could not believe that this brilliant stranger wished to court her; only a romantic woman like her aunt would believe that.

"哦,彭尼曼姑姑!"凯瑟琳吃惊地说,"他是个生人——我们不了解他。"

"我亲爱的凯瑟琳,你很清楚你喜欢他。"

"哦,彭尼曼姑姑!"凯瑟琳又说道。也许她确实喜欢他——尽管这件事对于她来说似乎不适宜讨论。不过她无法相信这样一个出众的陌生人想要追求她;只有她姑姑那样浪漫的女人才会这么想。

frightened *adj. in a state of fear*; *afraid*; *scared.* 恐惧的;害怕的;受惊的。

3
Who is Morris Townsend?

Half an hour after the two young men had left, Doctor Sloper came into the parlour.

'Mr Morris Townsend has just been here, Austin,' Mrs Penniman told her brother. 'What a pity you missed him.'

'Who in the world is Mr Morris Townsend?'

'The gentleman at Elizabeth's party who liked Catherine so much,' said Mrs Penniman.

'Oh, his name is Morris Townsend, is it?' the Doctor said. He looked at Catherine. 'And did he come here to ask you to marry him?'

'Oh, father!' murmured Catherine, turning away.

'I hope he won't do that without your permission,' said Mrs Penniman.

'My dear, he seems to have yours,' her brother answered. 'The next time he comes, you should call me. He might like to see me.'

Morris Townsend came again five days later, but Doctor Sloper was not at home at the time. Catherine was with her aunt when a servant announced the young man's name. Mrs Penniman sent her niece into the parlour alone.

'This time it's for you—for you only,' she said.

So Catherine saw Mr Townsend alone, sitting with him

3.　莫里斯·汤森是谁？

　　两个年轻人走后半个小时，斯洛珀医生进了客厅。

　　"莫里斯·汤森先生刚来过，奥斯汀，"彭尼曼夫人对弟弟说，"可惜你没见到。"

　　"莫里斯·汤森先生到底是谁？"

　　"伊丽莎白晚会上的那个年轻人，他很喜欢凯瑟琳。"彭尼曼夫人说。

　　"哦，他叫莫里斯·汤森，对吧？"医生说。他看着凯瑟琳，"他来这里是向你求婚吗？"

　　"哦，爸爸！"凯瑟琳低声埋怨着，转身走开了。

　　"我希望没有你的同意他不会那么做。"彭尼曼夫人说。

　　"亲爱的，他好像已经得到你的同意了。"她弟弟回答道，"下次他来的时候，你应该叫上我。他也许乐意见我。"

　　五天后莫里斯·汤森再次来访，不过当时斯洛珀医生刚好不在家。仆人通报来客姓名的时候，凯瑟琳正和她姑姑在一起。彭尼曼夫人让侄女独自到客厅里去。

　　"这次是为你而来——只为你一个人。"她说。

　　所以凯瑟琳独自一人和汤森先生相见，

what a pity (that) ... 真遗憾。**turn away** *leave; go away.* 离开，走开。

in the front parlour, for more than an hour. He seemed more at home this time—making himself very comfortable and looking around with interest at the room and the furniture. His talk was light, easy and friendly. 'Tell me about yourself,' he said to her, with his charming smile.

Catherine had very little to tell, but she told him of her love of music and the theatre, and how she did not really enjoy reading. Morris Townsend agreed with her that books were boring—he had been to places that people had written about, and they were not at all as they had been described. He had also seen all the famous actors in London and Paris, but the actors were always like the writers— they were never true to real life. He liked everything to be natural. Suddenly he stopped, looking at Catherine with his smile.

'That's what I like you for; you are so natural,' he said. 'You see I am natural myself.'

He went on to talk about his great love of music and singing. 'I sing a little myself,' he added; 'some day I will show you. Not today, but some other time.'

And then he got up to go. He had perhaps talked more about himself than about Catherine, but the truth was that Catherine had not noticed. She was thinking only that 'some other time' had a delightful sound. It seemed to suggest many more meetings in the future.

Catherine felt it was her duty to tell her father that

他们在前厅坐了一个多小时。他这次似乎更随意——他很放松，饶有兴致地打量着房间和家具。他的谈话也轻松、随意而且友好。"跟我说说你自己吧。"他对她说，露出了迷人的笑容。

凯瑟琳没多少可说的，不过她还是告诉他自己对音乐和戏剧的热爱，以及她不那么喜欢读书。莫里斯·汤森同意她的看法，认为书很枯燥——他去过书里提到的那些地方，跟书中描写的一点儿都不一样。伦敦和巴黎所有的著名演员他也都见过，这些演员和那些作家都一个样——都不忠实于真实的生活。他喜欢一切自然的东西。突然，他停了下来，面带微笑地看着凯瑟琳。

"这就是我喜欢你的地方；你这么淳朴。"他说，"你看，我本人并不矫揉造作。"

他继续讲他有多么喜爱音乐和歌唱。"我自己也唱唱歌，"他加了一句，"改天我唱给你听。今天不行了，改天。"

然后他就站起来走了。也许他谈论自己比谈论凯瑟琳还多，不过实际上凯瑟琳根本没注意到。她只是在想"改天"会听到令人愉快的歌声。这似乎意味着以后他们还会见很多次。

凯瑟琳觉得自己有责任把莫里斯·汤

at home *at one's ease, as if in one's own home.*（像在自己家里一样）自在，无拘束。**true to sth.** *being or acting as one would expect from sth.* 符合某事物的；忠实地反映某事物的。

Mr Morris Townsend had called again—though it made her feel ashamed and uncomfortable. She announced the fact very suddenly, as soon as the Doctor came into the house, and then immediately tried to leave the room. Her father stopped her just as she reached the door.

'Well, my dear, did he ask you to marry him today?' the Doctor said.

Catherine had no answer ready. She wanted to be amused, as her father was amused, but she also wanted to be a little sharp, so that he would not ask the question again. She did not like it—it made her unhappy.

'Perhaps he will do it next time,' she said, with a little laugh; and she quickly got out of the room.

The Doctor stood staring. He wondered whether his daughter was serious, and decided to find out more about this handsome young man. The next time he saw his sister Elizabeth, he asked her about Morris Townsend.

'Lavinia has already been to ask me about him,' Mrs Almond said.

'What did you tell her?' the Doctor asked.

'What I tell you—that I know very little of him.'

'How disappointing for Lavinia,' said the Doctor. 'She would like him to have some romantic secret in his past. I hear that he is a distant cousin of Arthur Townsend.'

'Yes, though it seems that there are Townsends and Townsends—some rather better than others. Arthur's

森先生再次造访的事情告诉父亲——尽管这使她感到害臊和不安。医生一进屋,她就突然宣布了这件事,然后就想立刻离开房间。她刚走到门口就被她父亲拦住了。

"嗯,亲爱的,他今天向你求婚了吗?"医生说。

凯瑟琳对这个问题毫无准备。她想愉快点儿,像她父亲那样,但她还想尖刻点儿,这样他就不会再问这个问题了。她不喜欢这个问题——这令她不愉快。

"也许下次他会这么做。"她轻轻一笑,说道;然后迅速离开了房间。

医生站在那里愣了半天。他不知道女儿是不是认真的,后来他决定去了解更多有关这个英俊青年的情况。他再次看到妹妹伊丽莎白的时候,就向她问起了莫里斯·汤森。

"拉维尼娅已经向我问过他的情况了。"阿尔蒙德夫人说道。

"你告诉她什么了?"医生问。

"就是我跟你说的——我对他不太了解。"

"拉维尼娅该有多失望啊,"医生说,"她希望他过去的人生经历中会有一些浪漫的秘密。我听说他是阿瑟·汤森的远房表兄。"

"是啊,不过好像到处都是姓汤森的人——有一些比另一些要好多了。阿瑟的

sharp *adj.* (*derog.*) *intended or intending to criticize, injure, etc.; harsh; severe.* (贬)蓄意批评、中伤等的;尖刻的;严厉的。

mother knows very little about him; only some story that he has been 'wild' in the past. I know his sister a little. Her name is Mrs Montgomery; she is a widow, with five children and not much money. '

'What is his profession?' asked the Doctor.

' He hasn't got any; he is looking for something. I believe he was once in the Navy. '

'Once? What is his age?'

' More than thirty, I think. Arthur told me that he inherited a little money—which is perhaps why he left the Navy—and that he spent it all in a few years. He travelled all over the world, lived in foreign countries, amused him-self. He has recently come back to America, and he told Arthur that he now wants to start his life seriously. '

'Is he serious about Catherine, then?'

'I don't see why you are surprised,' said Mrs Almond. 'It seems to me that you have never been fair to Catherine. You must remember that she will one day have thirty thou-sand dollars a year. '

The Doctor looked at his sister for a moment. 'I see that you remember it. '

Mrs Almond blushed. 'I don't mean that is the only good thing about her; I simply mean that it is important. You seem to think that nobody will ever want to marry her. '

'Why should I think differently, Elizabeth?' the Doctor said. ' How many young men have come courting

母亲对他也不太了解；只有一些传闻说他以前曾经'野'过一阵。他姐姐的情况我也知道一点儿。她叫蒙哥马利夫人；是个寡妇，带着五个孩子，没什么钱。"

"他是干什么的？"医生问道。

"他没工作；正在找事做。我想他以前在海军服过役。"

"以前？他多大了？"

"30多岁吧，我想。阿瑟告诉我他继承了一点儿钱——也许就是因为这个他才离开海军的——没出几年他就把这笔钱花光了。他周游世界，住在国外，活得挺快活。他最近才回到美国，他告诉阿瑟现在他想认认真真地过日子了。"

"那么他对凯瑟琳是认真的喽？"

"我不明白你为什么感到惊讶，"阿尔蒙德夫人说，"我觉得你从来没有公平地对待过凯瑟琳。你应该记住将来有一天凯瑟琳会有一年3万美元的进项。"

医生看了他妹妹一会儿："我知道你是记得的。"

阿尔蒙德夫人的脸一下子红了："我不是说她只有那一样好处；我只是想说那很重要。你好像觉得没人愿意娶她似的。"

"为什么我会和你想的不同呢，伊丽莎白？"医生说，"就算凯瑟琳将来会有这么一笔财富，又有多少年轻人来追求她呢？一个

wild *adj. out of control, undisciplined.* 不守规矩的；失去控制的。**the Navy** *warships of a specific country with their crews and the organization that administers them.* 海军部队。

37

Catherine, even with her expected fortune? None—which is why Lavinia is so charmed that there is now a lover in the house. It is the first time.'

'I think young men are rather afraid of Catherine,' said the Doctor's wiser sister. 'She seems older than they are— she is so large, and she dresses so richly. An older, more experienced man would recognize all the good things in her character, and would find her delightful.'

'And Mr Townsend? What are his reasons for courting Catherine? Is he sincere in liking her?'

'It is very possible that he is sincere. Lavinia is sure of it.'

Doctor Sloper thought for a moment. 'If he does not work, what are his means?'

'I have no idea. He lives with his sister and her children on Second Avenue.'

'A widow, with five children? Do you mean he lives *upon* her?'

Mrs Almond looked at her brother a little impatiently. 'Why not ask Mrs Montgomery yourself?' she said.

'Perhaps I will,' said the Doctor.

* * *

Doctor Sloper was more amused than annoyed by the idea of Mr Townsend courting his daughter. He was quite willing to believe the best of the young man. And if he was a sincere, honest man, it did not matter if he was poor, since

也没有——所以拉维尼娅才会这么热衷，家里现在来了个情人。这可是头一次。"

"我觉得小伙子们都很害怕凯瑟琳，"医生的这位更聪明的妹妹说，"她看起来比他们大——她个头这么大，穿得又华丽。只有年龄大一点儿、经验更丰富的男人才会发现她性格中所有那些美好的东西，也才会发现她是个惹人喜爱的姑娘。"

"那么汤森先生呢？他为什么会追求凯瑟琳？他真的喜欢她吗？"

"他很有可能是认真的。拉维尼娅确信是这样的。"

斯洛珀医生想了一会儿："他要是不工作，靠什么生活？"

"我不知道。他和他姐姐还有她的孩子们一起住在第二大道。"

"一个寡妇，带着五个孩子？你的意思是他靠她养活？"

阿尔蒙德夫人有点儿不耐烦地看着她哥哥。"你为什么不自己去问问蒙哥马利夫人呢？"她说。

"也许我会去的。"医生说。

* * *

想到汤森先生追求他的女儿，斯洛珀医生与其说是生气倒不如说是感到有趣。他很愿意往最好的地方去想这个年轻人。如果他真心实意，为人又诚实，那么他穷点儿

be sure of *not doubt or seem to doubt what one believes, knows, etc.* 无疑；确信；自信；有把握。**means** *n. money; wealth; resources.* 金钱；财富；财源。**live upon** *depend on sth./sb. for a financial source.* 靠某种经济来源生活。

Catherine had no need of a rich husband.

'The next time he comes,' he told Mrs Penniman, 'you must invite him to dinner.'

Mrs Penniman was happy to pass on her brother's invitation, which Morris Townsend accepted, and the dinner was arranged. Two or three other people were invited as well, and although Doctor Sloper talked very little to the young man during the meal, he watched him carefully. At the end of the meal, when the ladies had gone up to the parlour, leaving the men to their drinking, the Doctor gave him some wine and asked him several questions. Morris Townsend was happy to talk, and the Doctor sat quietly, watching his bright, handsome face.

'He is clever, a good talker, and very self-confident,' Catherine's father thought. 'And he dresses very well. But I don't think I like him.'

The Doctor, however, kept his thoughts to himself.

Later, when the men joined the ladies in the parlour, Morris Townsend went over to Catherine, who was standing before the fire in her red evening dress.

'Your father doesn't like me,' said the young man.

'I don't see how you know,' said Catherine, blushing.

'I can feel these things. You ask him and you will see.'

'I would rather not ask him, if there is any danger of his saying what you think.'

Morris gave her a sad little smile. 'So you will allow him

也没关系,反正凯瑟琳并不需要一个有钱的丈夫。

"下次他来,"他告诉彭尼曼夫人,"你一定要请他来吃晚饭。"

彭尼曼夫人很高兴地转达了弟弟的邀请,莫里斯·汤森接受了邀请,晚宴也安排下了。还邀请了两三个其他的人,虽然斯洛珀医生在进餐时没跟这个年轻人说什么话,他还是仔细地观察了他。晚餐到了最后,女士们都到客厅里去了,留下男人们继续喝酒,医生给他倒了一些葡萄酒,又问了他几个问题。莫里斯·汤森喜欢说话,医生静静地坐在那里,看着他那快乐英俊的脸。

"他是个聪明人,会说话,也很自信。"凯瑟琳的父亲想,"他穿得也很好。可是我想我不喜欢他。"

不过,医生只是心里这么想而已。

后来,当男人们加入到客厅的女士们中时,莫里斯·汤森走到身穿红色晚装、站在壁炉前的凯瑟琳那里。

"你父亲不喜欢我。"年轻人说。

"我不明白你是怎么知道的。"凯瑟琳涨红了脸说。

"我可以感觉到。你问问他就知道了。"

"要是他说的真的和你想的一样,我宁愿不去问他。"

莫里斯有些悲伤地朝她笑了笑:"那你

pass sth. on (to sb.) *hand or give sth. (to sb. else), esp. after receiving or using it oneself.* 将某物传、交、给(某人)(尤指自己收到或用过之后)。**would rather … (than)** (*usu. shortened to 'd rather*) *prefer to.* (通常略作 'd rather)宁愿;宁可;较喜欢。

to say things against me, and not tell him he is wrong?'

'I never argue with him,' said Catherine. 'And he won't say anything against you. He doesn't know you enough.'

Morris Townsend gave a loud laugh, and Catherine began to blush again.

'I shall never talk about you,' she said.

'That is very well; but I would prefer you to say that it doesn't matter what your father thinks.'

'But it would matter! I couldn't say that!' the girl cried.

He stared at her, smiling a little, and just for a moment there was an impatient look in those fine eyes. But he spoke softly and sadly. 'Then I must try to make him like me.'

* * *

The next time the Doctor visited Mrs Almond, he told her that he had now met Morris Townsend.

· 'He is certainly a fine-looking young man,' he said.

'But what do you think of him, as a father?' Mrs Almond asked. 'Lavinia tells me that Catherine is in love.'

'Well, she must stop being in love. He is not a gentleman. He is extremely charming, and completely insincere.'

'You have decided very quickly,' said Mrs Almond.

'Not at all. I have been studying people for a lifetime, and am now quite able to make a judgement in a single evening.'

'Very possibly you are right. But the thing is for Catherine to see it.'

'I will give her a pair of glasses!' said the Doctor.

42

就听凭他说不利于我的话,而不指出他的错误吗?"

"我从不和他争论,"凯瑟琳说,"他不会说不利于你的话。他对你还不够了解。"

莫里斯·汤森大笑了起来,凯瑟琳的脸又红了。

"我不会谈论你的。"她说。

"那很好,不过我更愿意你说你父亲怎么想都没关系。"

"当然有关系!我不能那么说!"女孩儿叫道。

他凝视着她,微微一笑,那双好看的眼睛里闪过一丝不耐烦的神情。不过他说话时声音温柔而悲伤:"那我只好想法让他喜欢我了。"

* * *

医生再次拜访阿尔蒙德夫人的时候,他告诉她说他已经见过莫里斯·汤森了。

"他的确是个相貌堂堂的年轻人。"他说。

"但作为父亲,你觉得他怎么样?"阿尔蒙德夫人问道,"拉维尼娅告诉我凯瑟琳坠入情网了。"

"嗯,她必须结束这场恋爱。他不是个绅士。他很有吸引力,但一点儿也不真诚。"

"你的决定作得太快了。"阿尔蒙德夫人说。

"一点儿也不快。我一生都在研究人,现在只要一个晚上我就能作出判断。"

"很有可能你是正确的。但这样的事情得由凯瑟琳自己去看明白。"

"我会给她一副眼镜的!"医生说。

against *prep. in opposition to（sb./sth.）.* 反对;违反;与……相反。**argue with sb.（about/over sth.）** *express an opposite opinion; exchange angry words; quarrel.* 争论;争辩;争吵。

4

Morris Townsend looks for a position

If it were true that Catherine was in love, she was certainly very quiet about it. She had told Morris Townsend that she would not mention him to her father, and so she said nothing about Morris's continued visits. It was only polite, of course, for Morris to visit after the dinner at Washington Square, and only natural for him to continue visiting.

These visits had quickly become the most important thing in Catherine's life. She was very happy. She did not yet know what the future would bring, and she was too modest to expect anything. She was just grateful for the present— the sound of his voice, the words he spoke to her, the expression of his face.

Doctor Sloper suspected Morris Townsend's visits, and noticed how quiet Catherine had become.

'What is going on in this house?' he asked his sister.

'Going on, Austin?' said Mrs Penniman.

'Why haven't you told me that Mr Morris Townsend is coming to the house four or five times a week? I am away all day, and I see nothing. '

Mrs Penniman thought for a moment. 'Dear Austin,' she said at last, 'I cannot tell a secret. '

'Whose secret? Catherine's? Mr Townsend's? If it is his,

4. 莫里斯·汤森求职

如果凯瑟琳真的恋爱了的话,那么她对这件事确实很低调。她告诉过莫里斯·汤森她不会向父亲提到他,所以对于莫里斯接下来的造访她只字未提。当然,莫里斯在华盛顿广场晚宴后来拜访只是出于礼貌,而他继续来访也很自然。

这些来访很快就成为凯瑟琳生活中最重要的事情。她非常开心。她还不知道未来会怎样,而且她太羞怯,也不敢奢望什么。她只是为现在的状况而心怀感激——他的声音,他对她说的话,他脸上的表情。

斯洛珀医生对莫里斯·汤森的来访有所察觉,也注意到凯瑟琳变得多么安静。

"这幢房子里发生了什么事?"他问他姐姐。

"发生了什么事,奥斯汀?"彭尼曼夫人说。

"你们为什么不告诉我莫里斯·汤森先生一周要来这里四五次呢?我整天都不在家,什么也看不到。"

彭尼曼夫人想了想。"亲爱的奥斯汀,"她最后说,"我不能把秘密说出来。"

"谁的秘密?凯瑟琳的吗?还是汤森先

suspect v. have an idea of the existence, presence or truth of (sth.); believe. 疑有;对……有所察觉。
go on (esp. in the continuous tense) take place; happen. (尤用于进行时态)发生;出现。

I think it is extremely foolish of you to have secrets with young men. You don't know where they will lead you. '

'I don't know what you mean,' said Mrs Penniman. 'I take a great interest in Mr Townsend; I don't hide that. But that is all. '

'It is quite enough. And what do you find so interesting about Mr Townsend? His good looks?'

'His misfortunes, Austin. I cannot tell you his story, but he would tell it to you himself, if he thought you would listen to him kindly. '

The Doctor gave a laugh. 'I shall ask him very kindly to leave Catherine alone. '

'Catherine probably says kinder things to him than that!'

'Has she said that she loved him? —do you mean that?'

Mrs Penniman stared at the floor. 'She doesn't talk to me about him. I think she is very happy; that is all I can say. '

'Townsend wants to marry her—is that what you mean?'

'He admires Catherine greatly,' said Mrs Penniman. 'And he says the most charming things about her. '

'And these misfortunes that you refuse to tell me about—did they make him poor?'

'It is a long story,' said Mrs Penniman, 'and all I can say is that he has been wild in the past. But he has paid for

生的？如果是他的，我想你和年轻男人有秘密实在是太愚蠢了。你不知道他们会把你引向哪里。"

"我不明白你的意思，"彭尼曼夫人说，"我对汤森先生很感兴趣；我并不否认。不过仅此而已。"

"这就够了。你觉得汤森先生哪里有趣？他英俊的外貌吗?"

"他的不幸遭遇，奥斯汀。我不能跟你讲他的经历，不过如果他认为你会友好地听他说话的话，他自己会告诉你的。"

医生笑了起来："我会很友好地请他离开凯瑟琳。"

"凯瑟琳也许会对他说些比这好听的话!"

"她说过她爱他吗？——你想说的是这个吗?"

彭尼曼夫人盯着地板："她没和我谈过他。我想她很开心；我只能说这么多。"

"汤森想和她结婚——你是这个意思吗?"

"他很喜欢凯瑟琳，"彭尼曼夫人说，"而且对她赞不绝口。"

"你拒绝告诉我的这些不幸遭遇——他是因此才落魄的吗?"

"说来话长，"彭尼曼夫人说，"我能说的就是他过去曾经荒唐过一阵子。但他已经

misfortune *n. bad luck.* 不幸；厄运。

47

it. '

The Doctor smoked his cigar in silence, then said, 'I am told he lives with his sister, and does nothing for himself. '

'He is looking very seriously for a position,' said Mrs Penniman. 'He hopes every day to find one. '

'Exactly. He is looking for it here, over there in the front parlour—the position of husband of a weak woman with a large fortune. That would suit him perfectly. '

Mrs Penniman got up and looked at her brother a little angrily. 'My dear Austin,' she said, 'you are making a great mistake if you think that Catherine is a weak woman!' And with this she walked away.

* * *

The family in Washington Square spent every Sunday evening at Mrs Almond's house. On the Sunday after his conversation with Mrs Penniman, Doctor Sloper went off to another room to talk to his brother-in-law about business. He came back later to find that Morris Townsend had arrived, and was sitting on a sofa beside Catherine. There were several friends of the family present, and it was easy for the two young people to sit and talk privately. The Doctor saw at once, however, that his daughter was painfully conscious that he was watching her. She sat very still, with her eyes down, blushing deeply.

Doctor Sloper felt so sorry for her that he turned his eyes away. 'Poor Catherine,' he thought. 'It must be very nice

为这付出了代价。"

医生默默地抽着雪茄，然后说："我听说他和他姐姐住在一起，可自己却游手好闲。"

"他正在很认真地谋职，"彭尼曼夫人说，"他天天都盼着能找到个职位。"

"的确。他是在这里找他的位置，就在客厅的前厅——当一个性格懦弱、又颇有家产的女人的丈夫。那对于他来说绝对合适。"

彭尼曼夫人站起身来，有点儿愤怒地看着她弟弟。"我亲爱的奥斯汀，"她说，"如果你认为凯瑟琳是个懦弱的女人，那你就大错特错了！"说完，她就走了。

* * *

华盛顿广场的这家人每个星期天的晚上都要到阿尔蒙德夫人家去。和彭尼曼夫人谈过话之后的那个周日，斯洛珀医生到另一间房间里和他妹夫谈论生意上的事情。等他后来回来的时候，发现莫里斯·汤森已经来了，而且正和凯瑟琳一起坐在沙发上。到场的还有几位家里的朋友，所以这两个年轻人坐在一起说悄悄话很容易。不过，医生立刻就发现他女儿已经痛苦地意识到他在观察她。她一动不动地坐在那里，眼睛朝下望着，脸涨得通红。

斯洛珀医生真替她感到难过，所以就把眼光移开了。"可怜的凯瑟琳，"他想，"对于

conscious *adj.* *aware; noticing.* 知道的；觉察的；注意到的。**be /feel sorry for sb.** *feel pity for sb.* 怜悯某人。

for her to have a beautiful young man court her. Perhaps I should give him another chance. '

A little later, when Morris Townsend was standing alone, the Doctor crossed the room towards him. The young man looked at him, with a little smile.

'He's amazingly conceited!' thought the Doctor. Then he said, 'I am told you are looking for a position. '

'Yes, I should like some work,' Morris Townsend replied. 'But I fear that I have no special talents. '

'You are too modest,' said the Doctor. 'I know nothing of you except what I see; but I see by your face that you are extremely intelligent. '

'Ah,' Townsend said, 'I don't know what to answer when you say that. You advise me, then, not to give up hope?'

The question seemed to have a double meaning, and the Doctor looked at him for a moment before he answered. 'No young man should ever give up hope. If he does not succeed in one thing, he can try another. '

Morris Townsend stared down at his shoes. 'Were you kindly suggesting a position for me?' he then asked, looking up and smiling.

This annoyed the Doctor, and he paused for a moment. Then he said, 'I sometimes hear of possibilities. How would you feel, for example, about leaving New York?'

'I am afraid I could not do that. I must find my fortune

她来说,有个英俊的年轻人追求她一定很好。也许我应该再给他一次机会。"

过了一会儿,当莫里斯·汤森一个人站着的时候,医生穿过房间朝他走去。年轻人面带微笑地看着他。

"他可真够虚伪的!"医生想。然后他说:"我听说你正在找工作。"

"是的,我希望找点儿事做。"莫里斯·汤森回答道,"但我恐怕没什么特殊才能。"

"你太谦虚了,"医生说,"我对你的了解就是我所看到的情况;不过从你的脸上我看得出你很聪明。"

"啊,"汤森说,"您这么说我真不知该怎么回答。那么,您是建议我不要放弃希望喽?"

这个问题似乎有着双重含义,医生看了他一会儿才回答:"年轻人永远也不应该放弃希望。如果他一件事做不成功还可以做另一件事。"

莫里斯·汤森低头望着自己的鞋子。"您是在好意向我推荐一个职位吗?"他接着抬起头笑着问道。

这令医生颇为恼怒,他停了半晌。然后他说道:"我有时能听到一些机会。比如,你觉得离开纽约约怎么样?"

"我恐怕不能那么做。我一定要在这个

double *adj. twice the (usu.) number or amount.* 两倍的;加倍的。**hear of sb./sth.** *be told about or have knowledge of sb./ sth.* 听到或知道某人或某事物。

51

in this city. You see,' added Morris Townsend, 'I have responsibilities here. I have a sister who depends on me.'

'Family feeling is very important,' said Doctor Sloper. 'I often think there is not enough of it in our city. I think I have heard of your sister.'

'It is possible, but I doubt it. She lives so very quietly.'

'As quietly, you mean,' the Doctor went on, with a short laugh, ' as a lady may do with several small children.'

'I help with my little nephews and nieces,' said Morris Townsend. 'I am their teacher.'

'That is very good, but it is not a career.'

'It won't make my fortune,'agreed the young man.

Later in the evening the Doctor spoke to Mrs Almond. 'I should like to see his sister,' he said. 'Mrs Montgomery. Mr Townsend tells me he teaches her children.'

'I will try and arrange it for you,' said Mrs Almond. 'I must say, he doesn't look in the least like a schoolteacher.'

And when Morris Townsend spoke to Catherine again later, he did not sound like a schoolteacher either.

'Will you meet me somewhere tomorrow?' he murmured. 'I have something particular to say to you—very particular.'

'Can't you come to the house? Can't you say it there?' Catherine asked, lifting her frightened eyes.

Townsend shook his head sadly. 'I cannot enter your

城市发家致富。您看,"莫里斯·汤森又加上一句,"我在这儿还有责任。我有个姐姐需要我养活。"

"家庭感情是很重要,"斯洛珀医生说,"我总觉得我们这个城市里这种感情并不多。我想我听说过你姐姐。"

"有可能,但我怀疑您是否真的听说过她。她生活得这么安静。"

"你的意思是,安静得就好像,"医生短促地笑了一声,继续说,"就好像一位带着几个年幼孩子的女士应该做的那样。"

"我帮着带小外甥和外甥女。"莫里斯·汤森说道,"我是他们的老师。"

"那很好,不过那不是个职业。"

"这不会让我致富。"年轻人表示赞同。

那天晚上晚些时候,医生和阿尔蒙德夫人谈了谈。"我想见见他姐姐,"他说,"蒙哥马利夫人。汤森先生告诉我说他教她的孩子们。"

"我试着替你安排一下,"阿尔蒙德夫人说,"我得说,他看上去可一点儿也不像个老师。"

当莫里斯·汤森后来又和凯瑟琳说话的时候,他听上去也不像个老师。

"明天你可以和我找个地方见面吗?"他低声说道,"我有些特别的事情要跟你说——很特别。"

"你不能来家里吗?你不能在那里说吗?"凯瑟琳抬起惊恐的眼睛问道。

汤森难过地摇了摇头:"我再也不能进

depend on sb. /sth. (*usu. not in the continuous tenses*) *get money or other help from sb. /sth.* (通常不用于进行时态)依靠;依赖。

doors again. Your father has insulted me. '

'Insulted you?'

'He dislikes me because I am poor. '

'Oh, you are wrong—you misunderstood him,' said Catherine, getting up from her chair.

'He laughed at me for having no position. I took it quietly; but only because he belongs to you. '

'I don't know what he thinks,' said Catherine. 'I am sure he means to be kind. You must not be too proud. '

'I will be proud only of you, my dearest,' said Morris, and Catherine blushed. ' Will you meet me tomorrow evening in the garden in the Square? It is very quiet there—no one will see us. '

Catherine hesitated. Young ladies did not go out alone in the evenings to meet young men in gardens. 'I am not—not very brave,' she said.

'Ah, then, if you are afraid, what shall we do?'

She hesitated again; then at last said, 'You must come to the house. I am not afraid of that. '

'I would rather meet in the Square,' the young man said. 'You know how empty it is, often. No one will see us. '

'I don't care who sees us. But leave me now. '

He left her. He had got what he wanted.

*   *   *

Catherine met the young man next day in the place she had

你的家门了。你父亲侮辱了我。"

"侮辱你?"

"他因为我穷就不喜欢我。"

"哦,你错了——你误会他了。"凯瑟琳从椅子上站起来说道。

"他嘲笑我没有工作。我平静地接受了;不过那只是因为他是你父亲。"

"我不知道他是怎么想的,"凯瑟琳说,"我相信他的本意是好的。你不应该太骄傲。"

"我只会因你而骄傲,我最亲爱的。"莫里斯说,凯瑟琳脸红了。"明天晚上你可以去广场的花园里和我见面吗?那里很安静——不会有人看到我们的。"

凯瑟琳犹豫了。年轻女士是不会在晚上独自到花园里和年轻男子相会的。"我不——不是很勇敢。"她说。

"啊,那么,如果你害怕,我们该怎么办?"

她又犹豫起来;最后她说道:"你一定要到家里来。我不担心那个。"

"我宁愿在广场见面,"那年轻人说,"你知道那里平常有多空。不会有人看到我们的。"

"我不在乎谁看到我们。不过你现在就走吧。"

他离开了她。他已经得到了想要的东西。

* * *

第二天,凯瑟琳和这个年轻人在她选的

hesitate *v. be slow to speak or act because one feels uncertain or unwilling; pause in doubt.* 犹豫;踌躇;迟疑;(因有疑虑而)停顿。

chosen—among the elegant furniture of a New York parlour. Mrs Penniman, as usual, left the two young people
alone to enjoy their romantic meeting.

'We must decide what to do,' said Morris.

He had already, on earlier visits, told Catherine that he
loved her. He had put his arm around her and taken kisses,
which had made her heart beat very fast. She felt deeply,
wonderfully happy, but she was also confused and a little
frightened. After Morris had kissed her, on his last visit,
she had begged him to go away, to let her think. She felt
his kisses on her lips for a long time afterwards, and she
could not think clearly at all. What would she do if, as she
feared, her father told her that he did not like Morris
Townsend?

Today, however, when Morris spoke about deciding
something, she felt that it was the truth, and said simply:

'We must do our duty; we must speak to my father. I
will do it tonight; you must do it tomorrow.'

'It is very good of you to do it first,' Morris answered.
'The young man—the happy lover—usually does that.'

'You must promise to be gentle with my father.'

'I shall try,' Morris promised. 'But do you know what
your father will say? He will tell you I want your money.'

'Oh!' murmured Catherine, softly. 'How wrong he is!'

Morris gave her a fond little kiss.

'I shall tell him that he is wrong,' said Catherine.

地方会面了——就在纽约的一间摆着高雅家具的客厅里。像平常一样，彭尼曼夫人让两个年轻人独自待在一起享受他们浪漫的约会。

"我们必须决定该怎么办。"莫里斯说。

他已经在早先的访问中，告诉过凯瑟琳他爱她了。他还曾经用胳膊搂着她，吻过她，那使她的心狂跳不已。她深深地体会到一种美妙的幸福感，但同时她又感到困惑并有点儿害怕。在莫里斯上一次来访时吻过她之后，她请求他离开，让她想一想。之后的很长时间，她都能感觉到他留在她唇上的吻，她已经完全不能清楚地想问题了。如果像她担心的那样，她父亲对她说他不喜欢莫里斯·汤森，那她该怎么办？

不过今天，当莫里斯说到要作决定的时候，她感到这种担心是真的，所以她轻描淡写地说：

"我们必须尽到责任；我们必须向我父亲说明。我今晚就说；你明天必须说。"

"你先说，这很好，"莫里斯回答道，"年轻男子——快乐的情人——通常都那么做。"

"你必须答应我，要和善地对待我父亲。"

"我会尽力的。"莫里斯答应道，"但是你知道你父亲会说什么吗？他会对你说我想要你的钱。"

"哦！"凯瑟琳低声道，声音很轻，"他太不应该了！"

莫里斯轻轻地给了她一个充满爱意的吻。

"我会告诉他，他错了。"凯瑟琳说。

beat v. (*of the heart*) *expand and contract rhythmically.* (指心脏)有节奏地舒张与收缩；跳动。**confused** *adj. unable to think clearly; bewildered.* 糊涂的；迷乱的。**duty** *n. moral or legal obligation.* (道德上的或法律上的)责任；义务。

'He will argue with you.'

Catherine looked at her lover for a minute, and then she said, 'I shall persuade him. But I am glad we shall be rich.'

Morris turned away. 'No, it's a misfortune,' he said. 'It is from that our problems will come.'

'If it is the worst misfortune, we are not so unhappy. I will persuade him, and after that we shall be very glad we have money.'

Morris listened to these sensible words in silence. 'You must speak for me on this; I cannot do it myself.'

Catherine, too, was silent for a while. She looked at Morris, who was staring out of the window. 'Morris,' she said, suddenly, 'are you very sure you love me?'

He turned round, and came to her at once. 'My own dearest, can you doubt it?'

'I have only known it five days,' she said, 'but now it seems to me something I could not live without.'

'You will never need to try.' He gave a gentle laugh. Then he added, 'There is something you must tell me, too.' Catherine had closed her eyes, and kept them closed. 'You must tell me,' Morris went on, 'that if your father is against me, you will still be faithful.'

Catherine opened her eyes and stared at him. She could give no better promise than what he read there.

"他会和你争论的。"

凯瑟琳看了她的恋人一会儿，然后她说："我会说服他的。不过我很高兴我们会富有。"

莫里斯转开身。"不，这是一种不幸，"他说，"这正是我们问题的根源。"

"如果这就是最不幸的情况，那我们就并非那么不幸。我来说服他，之后我们就会很高兴，因为我们有钱了。"

莫里斯默默地听着这些很实际的话。"你必须替我说这些话；我自己做不来。"

凯瑟琳也沉默了一会儿。她看着莫里斯，他正凝视着窗外。"莫里斯，"她突然说，"你确实爱我吗？"

他转过身来，立刻走到她跟前："我最亲爱的，你能怀疑这个吗？"

"我知道这一点才五天，"她说，"但是现在我好像已经离不开它了。"

"你永远也不需要尝试。"他轻轻地笑了笑。然后加上一句，"你也得告诉我一件事。"凯瑟琳已经闭上了眼睛，而且一直闭着。"你必须告诉我，"莫里斯继续说，"如果你父亲反对我，你依然不会变心。"

凯瑟琳睁开眼睛望着他。他在那双眼睛中读到了她最坚定的承诺。

persuade *v. cause sb. to do sth. by arguing or reasoning with him.* 说服或劝说某人做某事。**sensible** *adj. having or showing good senses; reasonable.* 识别力强的；合理的。

59

5

Doctor Sloper decides

Catherine listened for her father when he came in that evening, and she heard him go to his study. She sat quiet, though her heart was beating fast, for nearly half an hour; then she went and knocked on his door. On entering the room, she found him in his chair beside the fire, with a cigar and the evening paper.

'I have something to say to you,' she began very gently.

'I shall be happy to hear it, my dear,' said her father. He waited, looking at her, while she stared silently at the fire.

'I am engaged to be married!' Catherine said at last.

The Doctor did not show how surprised he was. 'You are right to tell me,' he said. 'And who is the happy man?'

'Mr Morris Townsend.' As she said her lover's name, Catherine looked at him. Then she looked back at the fire.

'When did this happen?' the Doctor asked.

'This afternoon—two hours ago.'

'Was Mr Townsend here?'

'Yes, father, in the front parlour.' She was very glad that she did not have to tell him her engagement had taken place in the garden of the Square.

Her father was silent for a moment. 'Why did

5. 斯洛珀医生的决定

那天晚上凯瑟琳听着父亲回来的声音，而且听到他走进书房里去了。她静静地坐着，虽然心跳得很快，她还是在那里坐了大约半个小时；然后她过去敲他的门。进到屋里的时候，她发现他正坐在壁炉边的椅子里，叼着雪茄烟，手里拿着晚报。

"我有话跟您说。"她开始说话，声音很温柔。

"乐意倾听，亲爱的。"她父亲说。他等待着，看着她，而她只是一言不发地盯着壁炉。

"我订婚了！"凯瑟琳终于说话了。

医生没有表现出多么惊讶的样子。"你能告诉我这个很好，"他说，"那么那个幸福的男人是谁？"

"莫里斯·汤森先生。"说出恋人名字的时候，凯瑟琳看着他。然后又看着壁炉。

"这是什么时候的事？"医生问。

"今天下午——两小时之前。"

"汤森先生来过这儿？"

"是的，爸爸，就在前厅。"她很高兴不需要告诉他自己是在广场花园里订婚的。

她父亲沉默了一会儿。"为什么汤森先

study *n. room, esp. in sb.'s house, used for reading and writing.* 书房（尤指家中的）。 **engagement** *n. agreement to marry.* 订婚。

61

Mr Townsend not tell me? It is his duty to speak to me first. '

'He means to tell you tomorrow. '

The Doctor smoked his cigar for a while. 'You have gone very fast,' he said, at last.

'Yes,' Catherine answered, simply. 'I think we have. '

Her father looked at her for a moment. 'I'm not surprised that Mr Townsend likes you. You are so simple and good. '

'I don't know why; but he does like me. I am sure of that. And I like him very much. '

'But you have known him a very short time, my dear. '

'Oh,' said Catherine, 'it doesn't take long to like a person—once you have begun. '

'Of course you are no longer a little girl. '

'I feel very old—and very wise,' said Catherine, smiling.

'I am afraid that you will soon feel older and wiser. I don't like your engagement. '

'Oh,' said Catherine, softly, getting up from her chair.

'No, my dear. I am sorry to give you pain; but I don't like it. Why didn't you speak to me first?'

Catherine hesitated a moment. Then she said, 'I was afraid you didn't like Mr Townsend. '

'You were quite right. I don't like him. '

'Dear father, you don't know him,' said Catherine

生不来告诉我？他有义务先跟我说。"

"他想明天跟您说。"

医生吸了会儿雪茄。"你们进展得很快。"他最后终于开口说道。

"是的，"凯瑟琳简单地回答道，"我想我们是很快。"

她父亲看了她一会儿："汤森先生喜欢你我并不觉得奇怪。你是这么单纯善良。"

"我不知道为什么；不过他确实喜欢我。我对此确信不疑。而且我也很喜欢他。"

"可是你认识他的时间很短，亲爱的。"

"哦，"凯瑟琳说，"喜欢一个人用不着太长的时间———旦你开始喜欢他。"

"当然你已经不再是小女孩儿了。"

"我觉得自己已经够大了——而且很明智。"凯瑟琳微笑着说。

"恐怕你不久就会感到年龄更大也更明智了。我不喜欢你订婚。"

"哦。"凯瑟琳轻轻地说，从椅子上站了起来。

"不，亲爱的。对不起让你痛苦了；不过我不赞成。你为什么不先和我商量商量？"

凯瑟琳犹豫了一会儿，然后说："我担心您不喜欢汤森先生。"

"没错。我不喜欢他。"

"亲爱的爸爸，您不了解他，"凯瑟琳柔

mean *v. have sth. as a purpose；intend sth.* 怀有某目的；打算；意欲。

63

gently. She remembered Morris's warning. 'You think he is only interested in my fortune.'

Doctor Sloper looked up at her, with his cold, reasonable eyes. 'I am not accusing Mr Townsend of that. You are an honest, kind-hearted girl, and there is nothing impossible in an intelligent young man loving you for yourself. But the main thing that we know about this young man is that he has spent his own fortune in amusing himself. There is good reason to believe that he would spend yours, too.'

'That is not the only thing we know about him. He is kind, and generous, and true,' said poor Catherine. She was not used to arguing, and her voice trembled a little. 'And the fortune he spent was very small.'

The Doctor stood up. He held her for a moment and kissed her. 'You won't think me cruel?' he said.

The question filled Catherine with fear, but she said, 'No, dear father; because if you knew how I feel, you would be so kind, so gentle.'

'Yes, I think I know how you feel,' the Doctor said. 'I will be very kind—be sure of that. And I will see Mr Townsend tomorrow. Meanwhile, do not tell anyone you are engaged.'

The next afternoon the Doctor stayed at home, waiting for Morris Townsend's visit. When the young man arrived, Doctor Sloper began at once.

'Catherine told me yesterday what has been going on

声说。她想起了莫里斯的警告。"您以为他只对我的钱感兴趣。"

斯洛珀医生抬起头看着他,目光冷淡而理智。"我并不是为这件事而指责汤森先生。你是一个诚实善良的女孩儿,聪明的年轻人爱上你这个人也不是不可能。但我们对这个年轻人的主要了解就是他把自己的钱都拿去享乐了。完全有理由相信他也会把你的钱花掉。"

"我们对他的了解不光是这一点。他心地善良,慷慨真诚,"可怜的凯瑟琳说。她不习惯和人争论,她的声音有些颤抖,"而且他花掉的钱也并不多。"

医生站了起来,把她搂在怀里抱了一会儿,吻了吻她。"你不会觉得我太不近人情了吧?"他说。

这个问题令凯瑟琳感到很害怕,不过她说:"不,亲爱的爸爸;因为如果您知道我的感受,您就会很和善、很温柔。"

"是的,我想我知道你的感受,"医生说,"我会很和善——相信我。我明天要见见汤森先生。另外,别告诉任何人你订婚了。"

第二天下午医生待在家里,等候莫里斯·汤森来访。那个年轻人一来,医生立刻就开始说话了。

"凯瑟琳昨天跟我讲了你们的事情,"他

reasonable *adj.* (*of people*) *ready to use or listen to reason; sensible.* (指人)讲理的;明事理的。
accuse *v. say that sb. has done wrong, is guilty (of sth.) or has broken the law.* 指责某人有错;控告;谴责。

65

between you,' he said. 'I am very surprised. It was only the other day that you first met my daughter. '

'It was not long ago, certainly,' said Morris. 'My interest in Miss Sloper began the first time I saw her. '

'Did it not start before you met her?' the Doctor asked.

Morris looked at him. 'I had certainly already heard that she was a charming girl. '

'Naturally, you will speak well of her,' said the Doctor. 'But that is not the only thing that is necessary. I told Catherine yesterday that I did not like her engagement. '

'She told me, and I was very sorry to hear it. I am greatly disappointed,' said Morris, looking at the floor.

'Did you really expect me to say I was delighted?'

'Oh no! I had an idea you didn't like me. '

'What gave you that idea?'

'The fact that I am poor. '

'It is certainly a fact I must consider,' said the Doctor, 'I do not dislike you, but you do not appear to be a suitable husband for my daughter, who is a weak young woman with a large fortune. '

Morris listened politely. 'I don't think Miss Sloper is a weak woman,' he said.

'I have known my child twenty years, and you have known her six weeks. But whether she is weak or not, you are still a man without a profession, and without money. '

'Yes, that is *my* weakness! You think I only want your

说,"我很吃惊。你是不久前才认识我女儿的。"

"没多久,当然了。"莫里斯说,"我第一次见到斯洛珀小姐的时候就对她产生了兴趣。"

"不是在你遇见她之前产生的吗?"医生问。

莫里斯看着他:"我当然已经有所耳闻,她是一个迷人的姑娘。"

"你自然会说她的好话,"医生说,"但这不是惟一必要的东西。我昨天跟凯瑟琳说我不赞成她订婚。"

"她告诉我了,听到这个真遗憾。我很失望。"莫里斯看着地板说。

"你真的希望我说我很高兴吗?"

"哦,不! 我知道您不喜欢我。"

"你为什么会那么想呢?"

"因为我穷。"

"这当然是我必须考虑的一个事实。"医生说,"我不是不喜欢你,不过你好像不适合作我女儿的丈夫,我女儿是一个拥有一大笔财产而又软弱的年轻女子。"

莫里斯礼貌地听着:"我认为斯洛珀小姐并不是个软弱的女子。"

"我的孩子我已经了解了 20 年,而你认识她才六个星期。但不管是不是软弱,你仍然既没工作也没钱。"

"是的,那是我的弱点!您以为我只想

consider *v. think about sb./sth., esp. in order to make a decision; contemplate sb./sth.* 考虑。
suitable *adj. right or appropriate for a purpose or an occasion.* 适合的;适宜的;恰当的。

daughter's money. '

'I don't say that. I only say that you are the wrong kind of man to marry my daughter. '

'A man who loves and admires her deeply—is that the wrong kind of man?' Morris said, with his handsome smile. 'I don't care about her fortune. Not in any way. '

'Fine words,' said the Doctor, 'but you are still the wrong kind of man. '

'You think I would spend her money—is that it?'

'Yes, I'm afraid I do think that. '

'It is true that I was foolish when I was younger,' said Morris, 'but I have changed now. I spent my own fortune, because it was my own. That does not mean I would spend Miss Sloper's fortune. I would take good care of it. '

'Taking too much care would be as bad as taking too little. Both ways would give Catherine an unhappy life. '

'I think you are very unjust!' said the young man.

'I can understand that you think that. '

'Do you want to make your daughter miserable?'

'I accept that she will think I am cruel for a year. '

'A year!' said Morris, with a laugh.

'For a lifetime, then. She will be miserable either way—with you or without you. '

Here at last Morris became angry. 'You are not polite, sir!' he cried.

'I'm afraid that is your fault—you argue too much. I

要您女儿的钱。"

"我并没那么说。我只是说你不是我女儿要嫁的那种人。"

"一个深爱她并敬重她的人——这样的人还不合适吗?"莫里斯说道,脸上仍然带着迷人的微笑,"我不关心她的财富。根本就不关心。"

"说得好,"医生说,"但你仍然不合适。"

"您以为我会花她的钱——是吗?"

"是的。恐怕我正是这么想的。"

"我年轻的时候确实很蠢,"莫里斯说,"但我现在已经变了。我把自己的钱花了,因为那是我自己的,那并不意味着我就会把斯洛珀小姐的钱也花掉。我会好好珍惜它的。"

"太过珍惜会和不加珍惜一样糟糕。两种方式都会使凯瑟琳过上不幸的生活。"

"我觉得您很不公平!"年轻人说。

"你这么想我可以理解。"

"您想让您的女儿痛苦吗?"

"我承认会有一年的时间她会认为我冷酷无情。"

"一年!"莫里斯说着,大笑起来。

"那么,就是一生。她无论怎样都会痛苦——不管是不是和你在一起。"

至此莫里斯终于生气了。"您可真没礼貌,先生!"他大声说道。

"恐怕那是你的错——你争论得太多

take care of *make sure that one/sb. is safe and well; look after oneself/sb.* 照看;照料;照顾。 **fault** *n.* *(responsibility for a) mistake or offence.* 过错;过失。

69

cannot accept you as a son-in-law, and I shall advise Catherine to give you up, which she will do. '

'Are you sure that she will give me up?' asked Morris.
'I don't think she will. She has gone too far ... to stop. '

The Doctor stared at him coldly for a moment.

'I will say no more, sir,' said Morris, and he left the room.

* * *

When the Doctor told Mrs Almond about his meeting with Morris Townsend, she thought that he had perhaps been too hard on the young man.

'Lavinia thinks I am being very cruel,' said the Doctor.

'And how is Catherine taking it?' said Mrs Almond.

'Very quietly. There have been no noisy tears, or anything of that kind. '

'I am very sorry for Catherine,' Mrs Almond said. 'Now she will have to choose between her father and her lover. '

'I am sorry for her too,' said the Doctor. 'It is just possible, of course, that I have made the greatest mistake of my life. So I shall go and visit Mr Townsend's sister, who will almost certainly tell me I have done the right thing. '

The visit was arranged for a few days later, and at the appointed time the Doctor arrived at a little house on Second Avenue, where Mrs Montgomery received him in a small front parlour.

了。我无法接受你做我的女婿,我会建议凯瑟琳放弃你,她会照做的。"

"您确信她会放弃我吗?"莫里斯问,"我觉得她不会。她已经走得太远……停不下来了。"

医生冷冷地盯着他看了一会儿。

"我没什么可说的了,先生。"莫里斯说完,离开了房间。

* * *

当医生把他和莫里斯·汤森会面的事情告诉阿尔蒙德夫人时,她觉得他也许对这个年轻人太苛刻了。

"拉维尼娅觉得我很无情。"医生说。

"凯瑟琳有什么反应?"阿尔蒙德夫人说。

"非常平静。她既没有哭哭啼啼,也没有其他任何这类的举动。"

"我真替凯瑟琳难过,"阿尔蒙德夫人说,"现在她不得不在父亲和恋人之间作出选择。"

"我也替她难过,"医生说,"当然,也可能我犯了一生中最大的错误。所以我得去拜访汤森先生的姐姐,她十有八九会告诉我,我做的是对的。"

这次见面定在几天后,医生在约定的时间来到了位于第二大道的一幢小屋,蒙哥马利夫人在一间小客厅里会见了他。

go too far *behave in a way that is beyond reasonable limits.* 做得过分。**appoint** *v. fix or decide on sth.* 约定;确定。

71

She was a little woman, with fair hair, and seemed rather alarmed by a visit from such a fine gentleman as Doctor Sloper. He explained the situation, but Mrs Montgomery was at first a little unwilling to talk about her brother.

'I can understand,' said the Doctor, 'that it is difficult for you to say unpleasant things about your own brother, but if my daughter married him, her happiness would depend on whether he was a good man or not.'

'Yes, I see that,' murmured Mrs Montgomery.

'And I must remind you,' said the Doctor, 'that after my death Catherine will have thirty thousand dollars a year.'

Mrs Montgomery listened with wide eyes. 'Your daughter will be very rich,' she said, softly.

'Exactly. But if Catherine marries without my consent, she will have only the ten thousand dollars she inherited from her mother. She won't get a penny from me. I will be happy to inform Mr Townsend of that.'

Mrs Montgomery thought for a while. 'Why do you dislike Morris so much?' she asked at last, looking up.

'I don't dislike him—he is a charming young man. But I dislike him as a son-in-law, who must take care of my daughter. She is so soft, so weak. A bad husband could make her very miserable indeed, because she is not clever enough or strong enough to fight her own battles. That is

她身材瘦小,长着一头金黄色的头发,似乎对像斯洛珀医生这种受人尊敬的绅士的来访感到吃惊。他解释了一下情况,但蒙哥马利夫人最初有些不大乐意谈论她弟弟。

"我能理解,"医生说,"说自己兄弟的坏话的确很困难,可是如果我女儿嫁给他,那她的幸福可就取决于他是不是个好人了。"

"是的,我明白。"蒙哥马利夫人低声说。

"我还必须提醒你,"医生说,"我死后,凯瑟琳每年会有 3 万美元的收入。"

蒙哥马利夫人听得瞪大了眼睛。"你女儿会很有钱。"她轻声说道。

"的确。但如果凯瑟琳不经过我的同意就结婚,那她就只有从她母亲那里继承来的 1 万美元。她不会从我这里得到一个子儿。我很乐意把这个情况通知汤森先生。"

蒙哥马利夫人想了一会儿。"你为什么这么不喜欢莫里斯?"她最后抬起头问道。

"我不是不喜欢他——他是一个很有吸引力的年轻人。但我不喜欢他当我的女婿,我的女婿必须照顾我女儿。她是那么温柔软弱。丈夫不好真的会令她非常痛苦,因为她还没有聪明或强壮到可以为自己而战斗

alarmed *adj. anxious or afraid.* 担心的;害怕的。
remind *v. inform（sb.）of a fact or tell（sb.）to do sth. he may have forgotten.* 提醒。

why I have come to you. You may not agree with me, of course; you may want to tell me to go away, but I think that your brother is selfish and lazy, and I should like to know if I am right. '

She looked at him in surprise. 'But how did you find out that he was selfish?' she said. 'He hides it so well. ' Then she turned her head away, and the Doctor saw tears in her eyes.

He waited for a moment, then said suddenly, ' Your brother has made you very unhappy, hasn't he? Tell me, do you give him money?'

'Yes, I have given him money,' said Mrs Montgomery.

'And you have very little money yourself, and also five children to take care of, I believe. '

'It is true that I am very poor,' she said.

'Your brother tells me,' said the Doctor, 'that he helps you with your children—he is their teacher. '

Mrs Montgomery stared for a moment, then said quickly, 'Oh yes; he teaches them—Spanish. '

The Doctor laughed. 'That must be a great help to you! So,' he went on, 'I see that I was right. Your brother lives on you, takes your money, and is extremely selfish. '

There were tears again in Mrs Montgomery's eyes. 'But he is still my brother,' she said, her voice trembling a little. 'You must not believe that his character is bad. '

The Doctor spoke more gently. 'I am sorry that I have

74

的地步。所以我来找你。当然,你可能不同意我的说法;你可能想让我走开,但我觉得你弟弟是个自私懒惰的人,我想知道我这么想对不对。"

她惊讶地看着他。"但你是怎么发现他自私的呢?"她说,"他隐藏得那么好。"然后她扭开头去,医生看到了她眼中的泪光。

他等了一会儿,接着突然说:"你弟弟让你很不愉快,是吗? 告诉我,你给他钱吗?"

"是的,我给他钱。"蒙哥马利夫人说。

"而你自己就没多少钱,还有五个孩子要照料,我想。"

"我的确很穷。"她说。

"你弟弟告诉我,"医生说,"他帮你带孩子——他是他们的老师。"

蒙哥马利夫人愣了半晌,然后很快地说:"噢,是的;他教他们——西班牙语。"

医生笑了。"那对你一定大有帮助! 那么,"他继续说道,"我看我是对的。你弟弟靠你养活,拿你的钱,而且极为自私。"

眼泪再次涌出蒙哥马利夫人的双眼。"但他还是我弟弟,"她说,声音有些颤抖,"你一定不会相信他人品恶劣。"

医生的口气更和善了。"抱歉让你难过

character n. mental or moral qualities that make a person, group, nation, etc. different from others.(个人、集体、民族特有的)品质,特性。

upset you. It's all for my poor Catherine. You must know her, and then you will see. ' He stood up to go.

Mrs Montgomery also stood up. 'I should like to know your daughter,' she answered; and then, very suddenly—'Don't let her marry him!'

And Doctor Sloper went away with these words ringing in his ears.

了。这一切都是为了我那可怜的凯瑟琳。你一定要认识她,那样你就会明白了。"他站起身准备告辞了。

蒙哥马利夫人也站了起来。"我很想认识您女儿,"她回答道;接着,很突然地——"别让她嫁给他!"

耳中回响着这些话,医生离开了。

ring *v. be filled with* (*sounds, etc.*). 响着(声音等)。

77

6

Catherine tries to be good

The Doctor was surprised, and even a little disappointed, to see that Catherine did not appear to be angry or upset about what had happened. He wanted to be kind to her, but she did not seem to want or need his kindness.

'I am glad I have such a good daughter,' he said, after several days had passed.

'I am trying to be good,' she answered, turning away.

'If you have anything to say about Mr Townsend, I shall be happy to listen.'

'Thank you,' said Catherine. 'I have nothing to say at present.'

He never asked her whether she had seen Morris again. She had, in fact, not seen him; she had only written him a long letter. 'I am in great trouble,' she wrote. 'Do not doubt my love for you, but let me wait a little and think.' But her thoughts were not at all clear. She could not really believe that her father would change his mind about Morris; she just hoped that in some mysterious way the situation would get better. Meanwhile, she felt she must try to be a good daughter, to be patient, and to search for a peaceful way out of their difficulty.

She received no help from her aunt in this search.

6. 凯瑟琳努力做好

医生感到惊讶,甚至有些失望地发现凯瑟琳对发生的事情没有显出生气或烦恼的样子。他想对她好点儿,但她似乎不想要或不需要他的好意。

"我很高兴有这样一个好女儿。"过了几天之后,他说。

"我正努力做好。"她回答,转身走开了。

"关于汤森先生,你要是有什么话要说,我乐意倾听。"

"谢谢,"凯瑟琳说,"目前我没什么可说的。"

他从没问过她有没有再见过莫里斯。实际上,她没再见到他;只给他写过一封长信。"我现在麻烦很大,"她写道,"不要怀疑我对你的爱,但让我等一等并想一下。"但她一点儿头绪都没有。她不能真的相信她父亲会改变对莫里斯的看法;她只是希望这种局面会奇迹般地好转。同时,她觉得自己必须努力做个好女儿,要有耐心,还要寻求一个和平摆脱困境的方法。

她没有从姑姑那里寻求到任何帮助。彭

in trouble *in a situation that involves danger, punishment, pain, worry, etc.* 在危险、受罚、苦难、忧虑 等 的 处 境 中。**change one's mind** *alter one's decision or opinion.* 改变决定 或 意见。**mysterious** *adj. full of mystery; hard to understand or explain.* 神秘的;不可思议的;难解的。

Mrs Penniman was enjoying all the excitement of the romance and had no sensible advice to offer poor Catherine. 'You must act, my dear,' she said. 'The important thing is to act.'

Mrs Penniman had also written to Morris, and had arranged to meet him secretly in a café on the other side of the city. She had not told her niece about this meeting, and so was a little embarrassed when Morris arrived and asked if she had a message for him from Catherine.

'Not exactly a message,' she said. 'I didn't ask her for one. But she will be true to you—until death.'

'Oh, I hope it won't come to that,' said Morris.

'My brother will not listen to argument.'

'Do you mean he won't change his mind?'

Mrs Penniman was silent for a moment, then she smiled at Morris. 'Marry Catherine first, and tell him afterwards!' she cried. 'That is the way I see it: a secret marriage.'

The young man stared at her. 'Do you advise me to do that? To marry her without her father's consent?'

She was a little frightened, but went on, 'If you marry Catherine, you will show my brother that he has been wrong about you. He will see that it is not just because you like—you like the money.'

Morris hesitated, then said, 'But I *do* like the money.'

'But you don't like it more than Catherine. And when he

尼曼夫人喜欢浪漫故事中所有激动人心的事情,可是她却不能给可怜的凯瑟琳提出任何明智的建议。"你必须采取行动,亲爱的,"她说,"重要的是行动。"

彭尼曼夫人也给莫里斯写了信,并且安排在城市另一头的一家咖啡厅里和他秘密见面。她没有告诉侄女这次会面的事情,所以当莫里斯到了之后问她有没有凯瑟琳给他的口信时,她有些尴尬。

"算不上口信,"她说,"我没向她要口信。不过她对你是真心的——至死不变。"

"哦,我希望不至于这样。"莫里斯说。

"我弟弟听不进意见。"

"您的意思是他不会改变主意吗?"

彭尼曼夫人沉默了一会儿,然后对莫里斯微微一笑。"先跟凯瑟琳结婚,然后再告诉他!"她大声说道,"我就是这么想的:秘密结婚。"

年轻人盯着她:"您建议我这么做吗?不经她父亲的同意就和她结婚?"

她有些吃惊,但还是继续说:"如果你和凯瑟琳结婚,那就是向我弟弟表明他对你的看法是错的。他会明白那不仅仅是因为你喜欢——你喜欢钱。"

莫里斯犹豫了一会儿,然后说:"不过我的确喜欢钱。"

"可是你不会喜欢它甚于喜欢凯瑟琳。

café *n. small inexpensive restaurant serving light meals and（in Britain usu. non-alcoholic）drinks.* 小餐馆(在英国通常不供应酒类)。

81

realizes that, he will think it is his duty to help you. '

Morris looked for some moments at the floor. At last he looked up and said, 'Do you think there is already a will leaving money to Catherine?'

'I suppose so—even doctors must die,' she replied.

'And you believe he would certainly change it—if I married Catherine?'

'Yes, but then he would change it back again. '

'But I can't depend on that,' said Morris.

'Do you want to *depend* on it?' Mrs Penniman asked.

He blushed a little. 'I do not want to injure Catherine. '

' You must not be afraid! Be afraid of nothing, and everything will go well. '

Mrs Penniman told Catherine that evening that she had had a meeting with Morris Townsend, and for almost the first time in her life Catherine felt angry.

'Why did you see him? I don't think it was right. '

'I was so sorry for him—and you wouldn't see him, my dear,' said Aunt Lavinia.

'I have not seen him because my father has forbidden it,' Catherine said, very simply.

This annoyed Mrs Penniman and she began to read the evening newspaper, so that Catherine would have to ask her about her meeting with Morris. But it was several minutes before Catherine finally spoke. 'What did he say?' she asked.

当他明白了这一点，他就会觉得有责任帮助你。"

莫里斯盯着地板看了一会儿。最后他抬起头来说："您认为他已经立了遗嘱把钱留给凯瑟琳吗？"

"我想是的——就是医生也会死的。"她回答道。

"那么您认为他一定会更改遗嘱吗——如果我和凯瑟琳结婚的话？"

"是的，但以后他还会改回来。"

"可是我不能指望那个。"莫里斯说。

"你想指望它吗？"彭尼曼夫人问道。

他有点儿脸红："我不想伤害凯瑟琳。"

"你不必害怕！什么都别怕，一切都会好的。"

那天晚上彭尼曼夫人跟凯瑟琳讲了她和莫里斯·汤森会面的事情，几乎是平生第一次，凯瑟琳感到生气了。

"您为什么要见他？我觉得这样不对。"

"我真为他难过——而你又不愿见他，亲爱的。"拉维尼娅姑姑说。

"我没见他是因为父亲不许我见他。"凯瑟琳说得很简单。

这令彭尼曼夫人颇为不快，所以她开始看晚报，这样凯瑟琳就不得不问她和莫里斯见面的事情。但过了好几分钟，凯瑟琳才终于开口。"他说了些什么？"她问。

will *n.* (*also testament*) *legal document in which a person states how he wants his property and money to be disposed of after his death*. 遗嘱。

'He said he is ready to marry you any day. '

Catherine made no answer to this, and after a few minutes Mrs Penniman added that Morris looked very tired.

Catherine got up from her seat and went to the fire.

Mrs Penniman hesitated for a moment. 'He said he was afraid of only one thing—that you would be afraid. '

The girl turned very quickly. 'Afraid of what?'

'Afraid of your father. '

Catherine turned back to the fire again. After a pause, she said, 'I *am* afraid of my father. '

Mrs Penniman got up quickly from her chair and went to her niece. 'Are you going to give him up, then?'

For some time Catherine stared at the fire and did not move. Then she lifted her head and looked at her aunt. 'Why do you make it so difficult for me?' she said. 'I don't think you understand or that you know me. You had better not have any more meetings with Mr Townsend. I don't think it is right. My father wouldn't like it, if he knew. '

' And you will inform him—is that what you mean? Well, I am not afraid of my brother. But I shall not try to help again—you are too ungrateful. I am disappointed, but your father will not be. Good night. ' And with this Mrs Penniman went off to her room.

* * *

Catherine sat alone by the parlour fire, lost in her

"他说他随时准备和你结婚。"

凯瑟琳对此没有作答,过了几分钟,彭尼曼夫人补充说莫里斯看起来很疲倦。

凯瑟琳从座位上站了起来,走向壁炉。

彭尼曼夫人犹豫了一会儿:"他说他只担心一件事——那就是你会害怕。"

女孩儿很快转过身来:"害怕什么?"

"害怕你父亲。"

凯瑟琳又转向壁炉。停了一会儿,她说:"我的确害怕我父亲。"

彭尼曼夫人很快地从椅子里站起来走向她的侄女:"那么你打算放弃他吗?"

有那么一会儿,凯瑟琳盯着炉火一动不动。然后她抬起头看着姑姑。"为什么您把事情弄得这么令我为难?"她问道,"我觉得您并不理解我,也不了解我。您最好别再和汤森先生碰面了。我认为这样不对。我父亲要是知道了会不喜欢的。"

"而且你还会告诉他——你是这个意思吗?好吧,我可不怕我弟弟。但我也不会再帮忙了——你太忘恩负义了。我很失望,但你父亲不会。晚安。"说完,彭尼曼夫人就回自己的房间去了。

* * *

凯瑟琳一个人坐在客厅的壁炉边,陷入

ungrateful *adj. not recognizing a kindness, service, etc.; not grateful.* 不领情的;不感激的;忘恩负义的。

85

thoughts, for more than an hour. She felt that to displease her father was a terrible thing, but she had made a plan and must go on with it. Her father was in his study, and it was eleven o'clock when she finally knocked on his door. Even when he answered her, she was too afraid to go in. After a while he came and opened the door for her.

'What's the matter?' asked the Doctor. 'You are standing there like a ghost!'

She went into the room, and her father looked at her for a few moments, waiting for her to speak. He then went back to his writing desk and sat down, turning his back on his daughter. At last she began:

'You told me that if I had something more to say about Mr Townsend, you would be glad to listen to it. '

'Exactly, my dear,' said the Doctor, not turning round.

'I would like to see him again. '

'To say goodbye?' asked the Doctor.

'No, father, not that; at least not for ever. '

'You have not finished with him, then?'

'No,' said Catherine. 'I have asked him to—to wait. '

Her father, turning round in his chair, looked at her with his cold eyes, and she was afraid he was going to be angry.

'You are a dear, faithful child,' he said, at last. 'Come here to your father. ' And he got up, holding his hands out towards her.

了沉思,就这样过了一个多小时。她觉得惹父亲生气是件可怕的事情,但她已经有了一个计划,必须进行下去。她父亲在书房里,她终于敲响他的门的时候,已经是 11 点了。甚至当他应声的时候,她都害怕得不敢进去。过了一会儿他过来给她开门。

"怎么了?"医生问道,"你站在那里像个幽灵!"

她走进房间,她父亲看了她一会儿,等着她开口。接着他回到写字台边坐下来,转过身背对着女儿。最后她终于开口了:

"您说过如果我还想说说汤森先生,您会乐意倾听。"

"没错,亲爱的。"医生头也没回地说道。

"我想再见他一面。"

"跟他道别?"医生问。

"不,爸爸,不是那样;至少不是永别。"

"那么你还没和他了断?"

"没有,"凯瑟琳说,"我要他——等等。"

他父亲在椅子里转过身,眼睛冷冷地望着她,她担心他马上就要发火了。

"你是一个可爱、忠实的孩子,"他最后说,"到爸爸这儿来。"然后他站起身,朝她伸出手。

displease v. make (sb.) feel upset or angry, annoy. 惹恼,触怒(某人);使生气。**finish with sb./sth.** end a relationship with sb. or a connection with sth. 与某人断绝关系;终止与某事物的联系。

87

The words were a surprise, and they gave her great happiness. She went to him, and he put his arm round her gently, and kissed her. After this he said, 'Do you wish to make me very happy?'

'I would like to—but I am afraid I can't,' Catherine answered. 'Do you want me to give him up?'

'Yes, I want you to give him up.'

He still held her, looking into her face. She looked away and they were both silent for a long time.

'You are happier than I am, father,' she said at last.

'I have no doubt that you are unhappy now. But it is better to be unhappy for three months, than miserable for the rest of your life.'

'Yes, if that were true,' said Catherine.

'It is true, I am sure of that.' When she did not answer, he went on, 'Don't you believe that I want the best for your future? I know how bad men can be—how false.'

She moved away from him. 'He is not false! What has he done—what do you know?'

'He has never done anything, that is the problem—he is lazy and selfish and thinks only of himself.'

'Oh, father, don't say bad things about him!' she cried.

'No, that would be a great mistake. You may do what you choose,' he added, turning away.

'If I see him again, will you forgive me?'

'No, I will not.'

这些话出乎她的意料,令她感到很幸福。她走到他跟前,他轻轻地伸出胳膊搂住她,并吻了吻她。之后他说:"你希望我非常高兴吗?"

"我愿意——但我恐怕不能。"凯瑟琳回答道,"您想让我放弃他?"

"是的,我想让你放弃他。"

他继续搂着她,看着她的脸。她把目光移开,两人都沉默了很长时间。

"您比我更快乐,爸爸。"她终于说。

"你现在不快乐,这我毫不怀疑。但三个月的痛苦比起后半生的不幸要好。"

"是的,如果真是那样的话。"凯瑟琳说。

"是真的,我肯定。"趁她还没回答,他继续说,"难道你不相信我想让你拥有一个最美好的将来吗?我知道男人会有多坏——有多虚伪。"

她从他身边走开。"他不虚伪!他做了什么——你知道什么?"

"他什么事都没做过,这就是问题所在了——他又懒惰又自私,而且只为自己着想。"

"噢,爸爸,别说他的坏话!"她大声说。

"不,那将是个极大的错误。你可以做你选择的事情。"他添了一句,转开身去。

"如果我再见他,您会原谅我吗?"

"不,我不会。"

forgive v. stop being angry or bitter towards sb. or about sth.; stop blaming or wanting to punish sb. 原谅;宽恕;饶恕。

89

'I only want to see him once—to tell him to wait. '

'To wait for what?'

'Until you know him better—until you consent. '

'I know him well enough, and I shall never consent. '

'But we can wait a long time,' said poor Catherine.

'Of course, you can wait until I die, if you like,' said the Doctor, quietly. 'Your engagement will have one delightful effect upon you; it will make you extremely impatient for my death. And think how impatient *he* will be, too. '

Catherine gave a cry of natural horror and stood staring. Her father's words had a terrible ugliness, and she did not know what to say. Suddenly, however, an idea came to her.

'If I don't marry before your death, I will not after,' she said. 'But I think that one day Morris might persuade you. '

'I shall never speak to him again. I dislike him too much,' said the Doctor. 'And you can tell Mr Townsend when you see him again that if you marry without my consent, I will not leave you a penny of my money. That will interest him more than anything else you can tell him. '

She looked at her father, and her eyes filled with tears.

'I think I will see him, then,' she murmured.

'Exactly as you choose. But if you see him, you will be an ungrateful, cruel child; and you will give your old father

"我只想再见他一面——让他等等。"

"等什么?"

"直到您更了解他——直到您同意。"

"我对他了解的够多了,而且我永远也不会答应。"

"但我们可以等很长时间。"可怜的凯瑟琳说。

"当然,如果你们愿意的话,你们可以一直等到我死。"医生平静地说,"你订婚对你会有一种可喜的作用;它会使你急切地盼着我死。再想想他会有多着急。"

凯瑟琳不由得发出一声惊恐的叫声,站在那里目瞪口呆。父亲的话里有一种可怕而丑陋的东西,她不知道该说什么好。不过,她突然有了个主意。

"如果您去世之前我没嫁给他,之后我也不会了,"她说,"但我想总有一天莫里斯可能会说服您。"

"我不会再跟他说话了。我太不喜欢他了。"医生说,"你要是再见到汤森先生,你可以告诉他如果你们未经我同意就结婚,我的钱一个子儿也不会留给你。你跟他讲什么都不如这更让他感兴趣。"

她看着父亲,眼中噙满泪水。

"那么我想我会见他的。"她低声说道。

"随你的便。但如果你见他,你就是个忘恩负义、冷酷无情的孩子;你会给你的老

effect *n. change produced by an action or cause; result or outcome.* 效应;结果;后果。**come to sb. (that ...)** *(of an idea) occur to sb.* (指看法)被某人想出。

the greatest pain of his life. '

The tears then ran down Catherine's face, and she moved towards her father with a little cry. But he only took her by the arm, went to the door, and opened it for her to go out.

After she had left, he walked around his study for a while, a little annoyed but also amused. 'My word,' he said to himself. 'I believe she will go on with it. ' He looked forward to seeing what would happen next.

父亲带来一生中最大的痛苦。"

　　泪水从凯瑟琳的脸上滑落，她轻轻地哭着走向父亲。但他只是拉着她的胳膊，走到门口，把门打开让她出去。

　　她离开以后，他在书房里踱了一会儿，既有些生气，又有些好笑。"依我看，"他自言自语道，"我相信她会继续下去的。"他等着看接下来会发生什么事。

look forward to sth. /doing sth. *anticipate sth. with pleasure.* 欣然期待某事物。

7
Catherine decides

The next day Doctor Sloper called Mrs Penniman into his study. 'I don't want Catherine, or you,' he said coldly, 'to see young Townsend again. And I expect you to obey me.'

'Do you wish to murder your child?' Mrs Penniman asked.

'No. I wish to make her live and be happy.'

'You will kill her: she had a terrible night.'

'She won't die of one bad night, nor of several.'

It was true that Catherine had had a terrible, sleepless night. But though her heart was breaking, she tried not to show her pain to the world. Mrs Penniman was very disappointed to see that there were no tears in her niece's eyes when she came down to breakfast.

That afternoon Catherine wrote to Morris, and the next day he came into the front parlour and stood before her. She thought that he looked more beautiful than ever.

'Why have you made me wait so long?' he asked. 'Every hour has seemed like years. Have you decided whether you will keep me or give me up?'

'Oh, Morris,' she cried, 'I never thought of giving you up!'

'What, then, were you waiting for?'

7. 凯瑟琳的决定

第二天,斯洛珀医生把彭尼曼夫人叫到了书房。"我不希望凯瑟琳,或者你,"他冷冷地说,"再去见年轻的汤森。我希望你听我的话。"

"你难道想害死你的孩子吗?"彭尼曼夫人问道。

"不,我想让她活得快乐。"

"你会要了她的命的:她昨晚过得太糟糕了。"

"她不会因为一个或者几个糟糕的晚上就丧命的。"

的确,那天晚上凯瑟琳过得很糟,整夜辗转难眠。不过,虽然她的心都碎了,她还是努力不在别人面前流露出痛苦的样子。彭尼曼夫人很失望地发现,她侄女下楼吃早餐的时候眼里并没有泪水。

那天下午,凯瑟琳给莫里斯写了封信,第二天他就来到了前厅,站在了她面前。她觉得他看起来从来没有这么好看过。

"为什么让我等了这么长时间?"他问,"每一小时就像好几年一样。你是决定和我在一起还是放弃我?"

"噢,莫里斯,"她哭道,"我从没想过要放弃你!"

"那么,你还在等什么?"

obey *v.* *do what one is told or obliged to do by* (*sb.*); *carry out* (*a command*). 服从;顺从;执行(命令)。

95

'I thought my father might—might look at it differently. But he—he looks at it still in the same way. '

'Then why have you sent for me?'

'Because I wanted to see you,' cried Catherine.

Morris watched her for a moment. 'Will you marry me tomorrow?' he asked, suddenly.

'Tomorrow?'

'Next week, then—any time in the next month. '

'Isn't it better to wait?' said Catherine.

'To wait for what?'

She did not know for what, but she felt afraid. 'Until we have thought about it a little more. '

He shook his head sadly. 'I thought you had been thinking about it these three weeks. Do you want to go on doing that for five years? My poor girl,' he added, 'you are not faithful to me. '

Catherine blushed, and her eyes filled with tears. 'Oh, how can you say that?' she murmured.

'You must take me or leave me,' said Morris. 'You can't please your father *and* me. You must choose between us. '

'I have chosen you,' she said.

'Then marry me next week!'

She stood staring at him. 'Isn't there any other way?'

'None that I know of. ' He turned away, walked to the window and stood looking out. 'You are very afraid of your

"我以为我父亲可能——可能会有不同的看法。不过他——他还是没改变态度。"

　　"那你为什么还把我叫来?"

　　"因为我想见你。"凯瑟琳哭道。

　　莫里斯看了她一会儿。"你愿意明天嫁给我吗?"他突然问道。

　　"明天?"

　　"那就下周——下个月任何时候。"

　　"等一等不是更好吗?"凯瑟琳说。

　　"等什么?"

　　她不知道要等什么,但是她感到害怕。"直到我们考虑得更多一点儿的时候。"

　　他难过地摇了摇头。"我想你这三个星期以来一直在考虑这件事。你还想再考虑五年吗? 我可怜的姑娘,"他又说,"你对我不忠实。"

　　凯瑟琳的脸涨红了,眼里噙满了泪水。"啊,你怎么可以这么说?"她低声说道。

　　"你必须要么接受我,要么就离开我,"莫里斯说,"你不能同时让你父亲和我都满意。你必须在我们中间作出选择。"

　　"我已经选择了你。"她说。

　　"那下周就和我结婚!"

　　她站在那儿望着他:"没别的办法吗?"

　　"就我所知,没有。"他转身走到窗前,站在那里朝外望着。"你非常害怕你父亲。"

send for sb. *ask or order that sb. should come.* 让某人来到。

father,' he said at last.

'I suppose I must be,' she said simply.

'Your fear of him seems greater than your love for me.'

'Oh, Morris,' she said, going to him.

After a while she told Morris what her father had said. 'If I marry without his consent, I shall not inherit any of his fortune. He told me to tell you that. He seemed to think—'

Morris blushed angrily. 'What did he seem to think?'

'That it would make a difference.'

'It *will* make a difference—in many things. But it will not change my love for you.'

'We shall not want the money,' said Catherine. 'You know that I have my own fortune.'

Morris was silent for a while. 'Do you think that he will be cruel to you for ever? That he will never change his mind about disinheriting you?'

'If I marry you, he will think I am not good.'

'Then he will never forgive you!' cried Morris.

Catherine suddenly felt lonely and afraid. 'Oh, Morris,' she cried, putting her head on his shoulder, 'you must love me very much. I will marry you as soon as you want!'

'My dear good girl!' he cried, looking down at her. She had given him her promise, but he was not quite sure what he would do with it.

他最后说。

"我想我一定是这样的。"她淡淡地说。

"你对他的害怕超过了对我的爱。"

"哦,莫里斯。"她说着朝他走过去。

过了一会儿她把她父亲所说的话告诉了莫里斯。"如果我不经他同意结婚,我就不能继承他的财产。他让我把这告诉你。他好像认为——"

莫里斯气得脸通红:"他好像认为什么?"

"那样做会让情况有所不同。"

"那样一定会令很多事情发生变化。但它不会改变我对你的爱。"

"我们不用要那笔钱,"凯瑟琳说,"你知道我有自己的钱。"

莫里斯沉默了一会儿。"你觉得他会一直对你那么无情吗?他永远不会改变剥夺你继承权的想法吗?"

"如果我和你结婚,他会认为我不好。"

"那他永远也不会原谅你!"莫里斯大声说道。

凯瑟琳突然感到孤独害怕。"哦,莫里斯,"她叫了一声,把头靠在他肩上,"你一定很爱我。只要你愿意我马上就嫁给你!"

"我亲爱的好姑娘!"他叫道,低下头望着她。她已经向他作出了承诺,可他却不太清楚该怎么对待这个承诺。

make a difference *have an effect*（*on sb./sth.*）. 对（某人或某事）有作用或影响。**disinherit** *v. prevent*（*sb.*）*from inheriting one's property*（*by making a new will naming another person as heir*）.（重立遗嘱,另定继承人以)阻止（某人)继承自己的财产;取消或剥夺（某人的)继承权。

99

*   *   *

For about a week, life in Washington Square continued much as before, and Doctor Sloper waited to see what would happen. He told his sister Elizabeth that he had never expected Catherine to give him so much excitement.

'It is not very kind of you,' said Mrs Almond, 'to find amusement in your daughter's situation.'

'I will take her to Europe,' said the Doctor, 'to give her some new ideas.'

'She won't forget him in Europe.'

'He will forget her, then.'

Mrs Almond looked serious. 'Would you really like that?'

'Extremely,' said the Doctor.

Mrs Penniman, meanwhile, arranged another secret meeting with Morris Townsend outside a church. She had been a little alarmed by her brother's coldness towards her.

'I think you should wait for a while before you marry,' she told Morris. 'Wait until my brother is less angry.'

The young man was very annoyed. 'Last week you advised me to marry immediately!' he said. 'Catherine has already agreed to this, so what can I do?'

'Catherine loves you so much that you can do anything,' said Mrs Penniman. 'You can change your plans, this way or that way, and she will not be upset with you.'

Morris looked at her, but said nothing, and soon after

* * *

大约有一周的时间,华盛顿广场的生活依然如故,斯洛珀医生等着看接下来会发生什么。他告诉妹妹伊丽莎白,他从未料到凯瑟琳会让他如此激动。

"你这样做不好,"阿尔蒙德夫人说,"你在你女儿的这种处境中找快乐。"

"我要带她去欧洲,"医生说,"给她一些新思想。"

"她在欧洲也不会忘记他。"

"那么他会忘记她。"

阿尔蒙德夫人严肃起来:"你真的喜欢那样吗?"

"非常喜欢。"医生说。

与此同时,彭尼曼夫人和莫里斯·汤森在一个教堂外安排了另外一次秘密会面。她对于弟弟对她的冷淡态度有些吃惊。

"我认为你应该等一阵子再结婚,"她告诉莫里斯,"直到我弟弟不太生气了为止。"

年轻人很恼火。"上星期你建议我立即结婚!"他说,"凯瑟琳已经答应了,那我能怎么办?"

"凯瑟琳很爱你,你怎么办都可以,"彭尼曼夫人说,"你可以改变计划,这样或那样,她不会烦你的。"

莫里斯看着她,但什么也没说,不久他

situation *n. set of circumstances or state of affairs, esp. at a certain time.* 状况,处境,局面,形势(尤指某时期的)。

that they parted.

Catherine, of course, knew nothing of her aunt's meeting with Morris, and she had not spoken to her father since the evening she went to see him in his study. At last, however, she told him that she had seen Morris Townsend again.

'I think we shall marry—before very long,' she said.

The Doctor looked at her coldly from head to foot. 'Why do you tell me that? It is of no interest to me.'

Catherine turned away for a moment; there were tears in her eyes. 'Oh, father,' she cried, 'don't you care?'

'Not at all. Once you marry, it is the same to me when, or where, or why you do it.'

But the next day he spoke to her in a different way. 'Are you going to marry in the next four or five months?'

'I don't know, father,' said Catherine. 'It is not very easy for us to decide.'

'Wait, then, for six months, and meanwhile I will take you to Europe. I would very much like you to go.'

This sign of her father's interest in her gave Catherine great happiness. 'It would be delightful to go to Europe,' she said. But her happiness soon disappeared when she realized that she would not see Morris for several months.

Mrs Penniman was not invited, and she understood very well why the Doctor had made this plan. 'He thinks the journey will make you forget Morris,' she told her niece.

Catherine could not decide whether to obey her father's

们就分手了。

凯瑟琳当然对她姑姑和莫里斯会面的事一无所知,自那晚去书房见过父亲之后,她一直没有和他说过话。不过,最后她告诉他,她又和莫里斯·汤森见面了。

"我想我们要结婚了——不久以后。"她说。

医生冷冷地把她从头到脚打量了一番:"你为什么告诉我这个?我对此不感兴趣。"

凯瑟琳转过头去,停了片刻;她的眼中含着泪水。"哦,爸爸,"她哭道,"您难道不关心吗?"

"一点儿也不。一旦你结婚,那么无论什么时间,或什么地点,或为什么你那么做对我来说都是一样的。"

但第二天他却用了一种完全不同的方式和她说话:"你打算在四五个月之内结婚吗?"

"我不知道,爸爸,"凯瑟琳说,"我们作决定不是那么容易的。"

"那就等六个月,在这期间我带你去欧洲。我很想让你去。"

父亲对她表露出的兴趣让凯瑟琳非常开心。"去欧洲会令人愉快的。"她说。但当她意识到会有几个月见不到莫里斯时,她很快就开心不起来了。

彭尼曼夫人没有受到邀请,她很清楚医生为什么要制订这样一个计划。"他以为这次旅行会让你忘了莫里斯。"她告诉侄女。

凯瑟琳不知道该不该服从父亲的意志。

part v. (cause sb. to) go away or separate from sb.(使某人)离开或与某人分离。sign n. thing that shows that sb./sth. is present or exists, or that sth. may happen. 痕迹;迹象;征兆。

wishes or not. She wrote to Morris and asked him to meet her in the Square. They met the next day, and during a long walk she told him about her father's invitation.

'He thinks I will forget you,' said Catherine.

'Well, my dear, perhaps you will. There are so many exciting things to see in Europe.'

'Please don't say that,' Catherine answered, gently. 'I am not interested in seeing Europe.'

'You should go,' said Morris. 'It will please your father, and perhaps he will forgive you and change his mind about disinheriting you.'

'And not get married for so long?'

'We can marry when you come back,' said Morris. 'You can buy your wedding clothes in Paris.'

* * *

They were away, in fact, for a year and during the first six months the name of Morris Townsend was not mentioned. The Doctor found much to interest him in Europe, but although Catherine was always quiet and obedient, she was, her father thought, a very unintelligent companion.

One day, at the end of the summer, they were walking together in a lonely valley in the mountains. It was beginning to get dark and the air was cold and sharp.

Suddenly the Doctor stopped and looked at Catherine.

'Have you given him up?' he asked.

The question was unexpected, but Catherine did not

她给莫里斯写信,约他来广场见面。第二天他们相见了,在长时间的散步过程中她给他讲了父亲的邀请。

"他以为我会忘了你。"凯瑟琳说。

"嗯,亲爱的,也许你会的。欧洲有那么多激动人心的东西可看。"

"请不要那么说,"凯瑟琳轻声地答道,"我对在欧洲观光没兴趣。"

"你应该去,"莫里斯说,"这会让你父亲高兴,也许他会原谅你,并且改变剥夺你继承权的想法。"

"那这么长时间不结婚?"

"我们可以在你回来后结婚,"莫里斯说,"你可以在巴黎买你的结婚礼服。"

* * *

他们实际上走了一年,在头六个月里,莫里斯·汤森这个名字从未被提起过。医生发现欧洲有很多令他感兴趣的东西,可是尽管凯瑟琳总是安静而顺从,她父亲却认为她是一个很愚钝的旅伴。

夏末的一天,他们一起沿着一条人迹罕至的山谷散步。天渐渐黑了,空气也冷得刺骨。

医生突然停住脚步看着凯瑟琳。

"你放弃他了吗?"他问。

这个问题问得突然,但凯瑟琳并没有犹

obedient *adj. doing what one is told to do ; willing to obey.* 服的;顺从的;听话的。**sharp** *adj. producing a physical sensation of cutting or piercing.* 刺骨的;凛冽的。

hesitate. 'No, father,' she answered.

He looked at her for some moments without speaking.

'Does he write to you?' he asked.

'Yes, about twice a month.'

The Doctor looked up and down the mountain, and said in a low voice, 'I am very angry.'

'I am sorry,' Catherine murmured. She felt lonely and frightened in this wild place.

'One day he will leave you,' said the Doctor. 'Alone and hungry, in a place like this. That's what he will do.'

'That's not true, father, and you should not say it,' she cried. 'It's not right!'

He shook his head slowly. 'No, it's not right, because you won't believe it. But it is true.'

Doctor Sloper did not speak of Morris again until the night before they sailed to New York. 'What are you going to do when you get home?' he asked suddenly.

'Do you mean about Mr Townsend?'

'About Mr Townsend.'

'We shall probably marry.'

'So you will go off with him as soon as you arrive?'

Catherine did not like the way he said this. 'I cannot tell you until we arrive,' she said.

'If I am going to lose my only child, I would like to know before it happens.'

'Oh father! You will not lose me,' said Catherine.

豫。"没有,爸爸。"她回答道。

他看了她一会儿,没说话。

"他给你写信了吗?"

"是的。大约一个月两封信。"

医生上上下下地看了看山,低声说道:
"我很生气。"

"对不起。"凯瑟琳喃喃地说道。在这荒
凉的地方,她感到孤独害怕。

"总有一天他会离开你,"医生说,"把你
一个人留在这样一个地方,忍饥挨饿。他会
那么做的。"

"那不是真的,爸爸,你不该那么说,"她
哭道,"那是不对的!"

他慢慢地摇了摇头。"是的,这样不对,
因为你不愿意相信。但这却是真的。"

直到他们乘船返回纽约之前的那个晚
上,斯洛珀医生再也没有提起过莫里斯的名
字。"你回到家之后有什么打算?"他突然问
道。

"你的意思是关于汤森先生的事吗?"

"是关于汤森先生的。"

"我们可能会结婚。"

"那么你一到家就会和他私奔?"

凯瑟琳不喜欢他说这话的方式。"我们
到了以后我才能告诉您。"她说。

"如果我会失去我惟一的孩子,我想在
事情发生前知道。"

"噢,爸爸!你不会失去我的。"凯瑟琳
说。

go off with sb. *leave one's husband, wife, lover, etc. in order to have a relationship with sb. else.* 离开丈夫、妻子、情人等另结新欢。

8

The last parting

C atherine did not 'go off' with Morris Townsend
when she arrived in New York, but she did hear
news of him from her aunt during her first evening home.
In fact, while she had been away, Morris had been a frequent visitor in Washington Square, taking tea with
Mrs Penniman and sitting in Doctor Sloper's study to
smoke cigars. Mrs Almond had told her sister that she was
behaving foolishly.

'You should not be so friendly with him, Lavinia,' she
said. 'He will make Catherine a bad husband. If he marries
her and she doesn't get Austin's money, he will hate her
for his disappointment, and will be cruel to her. The poor
girl will have a miserable life.'

But Mrs Penniman did not listen to her sister, and on
Catherine's return she told her niece that she had taken
good care of her lover while she had been away.

'And how is your father?' she asked. 'Has he changed
his mind about disinheriting you?'

'No. In Europe I saw that I shall never change him,'
said poor Catherine. 'I expect nothing from him now.'

'You have become very brave,' said Mrs Penniman,
with a short laugh. 'I didn't advise you to give up your
property.'

8. 最后的离别

　　凯瑟琳回到纽约后并没有和莫里斯·汤森"私奔",不过到家的第一个晚上她的确从姑姑那里听到了他的消息。实际上,在她离开的那段时间里,莫里斯经常到华盛顿广场来拜访,和彭尼曼夫人一起喝茶,坐在斯洛珀医生的书房里抽雪茄。阿尔蒙德夫人告诉过她姐姐这么做很愚蠢。

　　"你不应该对他这么好,拉维尼娅,"她说,"他不会是凯瑟琳的好丈夫。如果他和她结婚,而她得不到奥斯汀的钱,他就会因为失望而讨厌她,还会虐待她。这个可怜的女孩儿会生活得很凄惨。"

　　但彭尼曼夫人听不进妹妹的话,凯瑟琳一回来她就告诉她侄女,在她离开的那段时间里她把她的恋人照顾得很好。

　　"你父亲怎么样?"她问道,"他有没有改变剥夺你继承权的想法?"

　　"没有。在欧洲的时候我明白我永远没法改变他,"可怜的凯瑟琳说,"我现在对他不抱任何期望了。"

　　"你变得很勇敢了,"彭尼曼夫人笑了一声,说道,"我可不主张你放弃自己的财产。"

frequent *adj. happening often; habitual.* 时常发生的;惯常的。**property** *n. thing or things owned; possession(s).* 所有物;财产;资产。

'Yes, I am braver than I was. I have changed in that way—I have changed very much. And it isn't my property. If Morris doesn't care about it, then I don't care either. '

Mrs Penniman hesitated. 'Perhaps he does care about it. '

'He cares about it because he doesn't want to injure me, but he knows that I am not afraid of that. Besides, I have my own money; we shall have enough to live well. '

The next day Morris Townsend came to visit Catherine.

'I am very glad you have come back, ' he said. 'It makes me very happy to see you again. ' He looked at her, smiling, from head to foot.

When Catherine saw his handsome face again, she found it hard to believe that this beautiful young man was hers. She was very happy, and without waiting for him to ask, she told Morris about her father.

'We must not expect his money now, ' she said, 'and we must live without it. '

Morris sat looking and smiling. 'My poor, dear girl!' he cried.

'You must not be sad for me, ' said Catherine.

Morris continued to smile, and then he got up and walked around the room. 'Let me talk to him, ' he said. 'I want to prove to your father that he is wrong about me. '

'Please don't, Morris, ' said Catherine sadly. 'We must ask nothing from him. I know he will never change. '

"是的,我比以前勇敢了。我已经朝那个方向转变——我改变了很多。而且,那不是我的财产。如果莫里斯不在乎,我也不在乎。"

彭尼曼夫人犹豫了:"也许他在乎呢。"

"他在乎是因为他不想伤害我,不过他知道我不怕。而且,我有自己的钱;可以让我们过得不错。"

第二天莫里斯·汤森来看望凯瑟琳。

"我真高兴你回来了,"他说,"再次见到你真高兴。"他微笑着,从头到脚把她打量了一番。

凯瑟琳再次看到他那英俊的脸庞时,觉得很难相信这个俊朗的年轻人是她的。她很高兴,没等他问,她就跟莫里斯讲了父亲的事。

"我们现在不要指望他的钱了,"她说,"而且我们必须不靠它来生活。"

莫里斯坐在那儿,望着她微笑。"我可怜的宝贝儿!"他叫道。

"你不必为我难过。"凯瑟琳说。

莫里斯依然微笑着,然后站起来在屋中踱步。"让我跟他谈谈,"他说,"我想向你父亲证明他对我的看法是错的。"

"请不要这样,莫里斯,"凯瑟琳悲伤地说,"我们不要向他祈求任何东西。我知道他永远也不会改变的。"

prove *v. show that sth. is true or certain by means of argument or evidence.* 证明某事物属实;证实某事物。

111

'Why not?'

She hesitated for a moment. 'He is not very fond of me,' she said slowly. 'And I think he despises me. I saw it, I felt it, in England, just before we left. It is because he is so fond of my mother, who died so many years ago. She was beautiful and very, very clever—he is always thinking of her. I am not at all like her; Aunt Penniman has told me that. Of course it isn't my fault, but neither is it his fault.'

'You are a strange family,' said Morris.

'Don't say that—don't say anything unkind,' Catherine said. 'You must be very kind to me now, because, Morris,'—here she hesitated—'because I have done a lot for you.'

'Oh, I know that, my dear.'

'It has been terrible for me to feel so distant from my father—to feel that he despises me. I would be so miserable if I didn't love you. We must be very happy together! And, Morris, Morris, you must never despise me!'

This was an easy promise to make, and Morris made it. But for the moment he made no further promises.

* * *

Doctor Sloper spoke to both his sisters soon after his return. He told Mrs Penniman that he would never accept Morris Townsend as a son-in-law, and he told Mrs Almond that he was now no longer amused by Catherine, only annoyed.

"为什么不会?"

她迟疑了片刻。"他不太喜欢我,"她慢慢地说道,"我想他瞧不起我。我明白这一点,我们离开英国之前我就感觉到了。因为他太喜欢我母亲,可惜她许多年前就过世了。她美丽而且非常、非常聪明——他一直怀念着她。我和她一点儿也不像;彭尼曼姑姑跟我说过。这当然不是我的错,但也不是他的错。"

"你们一家人可真怪。"莫里斯说。

"别那么说——别说刻薄话。"凯瑟琳说,"你现在一定要好好待我,因为,莫里斯,"——说到这儿她迟疑了一下——"因为我已经为你做了那么多。"

"噢,我知道,亲爱的。"

"感觉和父亲那么疏远真让我难受——我觉得他瞧不起我。如果我不爱你,我会很痛苦。我们在一起一定要快快乐乐的!还有,莫里斯,莫里斯,你千万不要瞧不起我!"

作这样的承诺很容易,所以莫里斯答应了。但他暂时没有作进一步的承诺。

* * *

斯洛珀医生回来之后不久就分别找他的两位姐妹谈话。他告诉彭尼曼夫人他决不会接受莫里斯·汤森做他的女婿,他又告诉阿尔蒙德夫人他现在已经不再喜欢凯瑟琳了,只是很生她的气。

fond of sb./doing sth. *having a great liking for sb./doing sth.* 喜爱某人或做某事。**distant** *adj. not very friendly; reserved.* 不太友好的;不太热情的;冷漠的。

113

'She will never give Mr Townsend up,' said Mrs Almond.

'Then she will be very unhappy, and I can't prevent it.'

'Poor Catherine!' said Mrs Almond. 'We must be as kind to her as we can.'

Mrs Penniman arranged another secret meeting with Morris. They went for a long walk together, and she told him what the Doctor had said.

'He will never give us a penny,' said Morris angrily. After a pause, he added, 'I must give her up!'

Mrs Penniman was silent for a moment. Though she thought of Morris as a son, she was also a little afraid of him. 'I think I understand you,' she said, gently. 'But my poor Morris, do you know how much she loves you?'

'No, I don't. I don't want to know.'

'It will be very hard for Catherine,' said Mrs Penniman.

'You must help her. The Doctor will help you; he will be delighted with the news.'

'He will say, "I always told you so!"'

Morris blushed bright red. 'I find this all very unpleasant,' he said. 'A true friend would try and make it easier for me.'

'Would you like me to tell her?' Mrs Penniman asked.

'You mustn't tell her, but you can—' He hesitated, trying to think what Mrs Penniman could do. 'You can explain that I don't want to come between her and her

"她决不会放弃汤森先生的。"阿尔蒙德夫人说。

"那么她会很不幸,可我却无法阻止。"

"可怜的凯瑟琳!"阿尔蒙德夫人说,"我们应该尽量对她好些。"

彭尼曼夫人和莫里斯又安排了另外一次秘密会面。他们一起散步,走了很长时间,她把医生的话告诉他。

"他决不会给我们一分钱。"莫里斯生气地说。停了一下,他又继续说:"我必须放弃她!"

彭尼曼夫人沉默了一会儿。虽然她把莫里斯看作儿子一般,她也有些怕他。"我想我理解你,"她轻声说道,"不过,可怜的莫里斯,你知道她有多爱你吗?"

"不,我不知道。也不想知道。"

"这对凯瑟琳来说太难了。"彭尼曼夫人说。

"你必须帮她。医生会帮你;他听到这个消息会高兴的。"

"他会说:'我早就告诉过你!'"

莫里斯的脸涨得通红。"我觉得这一切太讨厌了,"他说,"真正的朋友会设法让情况变得对我容易些。"

"要我告诉她吗?"彭尼曼夫人问道。

"千万别告诉她,不过你可以——"他犹豫了一下,拿不定主意彭尼曼夫人能做什么,"你可以跟她解释,说我不想影响他们父

come between sb. and sb. *interfere with or harm a relationship between two people.* 干预或损害两人之间的关系;离间。

115

father. '

'Are you not going to come and see her again?'

'Oh no, I shall come again, but I want this business to end soon. I have been four times since she came back, and it's very hard work. '

'But you must have your last parting!' his companion cried. For Mrs Penniman the last parting between lovers was almost as romantic as the first meeting.

Morris came to Washington Square again, without managing the last parting; and again and again. Catherine did not suspect anything was wrong, and Mrs Penniman was too frightened to say anything to her. During each visit the poor girl waited for Morris to name the day of their wedding. But he never stayed more than a few minutes, and seemed so uncomfortable that at last she became worried.

'Are you sick?' she asked him.

'I am not at all well,' he said. 'And I have to go away. '

'Go away? Where are you going, Morris?'

He looked at her, and for a second or two she was afraid of him. 'Will you promise not to be angry?' he said.

'Angry! —do I get angry?'

'I have to go away on business—to New Orleans. '

'What is your business? Your business is to be with me. '

He told her a long story about a chance he had to make a

116

女的关系。"

"你不再来见她了吗?"

"哦,不,我还会再来,不过我想早点儿把这件事了结了。她回来后我已经来过四次了,这很不容易。"

"但你一定要最后道别一下!"他的同伴大声说道。对于彭尼曼夫人来说,恋人之间最后的离别几乎和初会一样浪漫。

* * *

莫里斯又来到了华盛顿广场,不过并没有做到最后分手,而是一再光顾。凯瑟琳还没有觉察出任何异样,而彭尼曼夫人太担心了,什么也没跟她说。每次会面,可怜的女孩儿都等着莫里斯定下他们婚礼的日子。可是他总是待不上几分钟就走,而且显得心神不宁,最后她开始担心了。

"你病了吗?"她问他。

"我不太舒服,"他说,"我要走了。"

"走? 去哪里,莫里斯?"

他看着她,有那么一两秒种她觉得有些怕他。"答应我不要生气好吗?"他说。

"生气! ——我生气了吗?"

"我要离开去办点儿事——去新奥尔良。"

"办什么事? 你要办的事就是和我在一起。"

他给她讲了一个很长的故事,说有个好

manage v. *succeed in doing* (*sth.*); *cope* (*with sth.*). 做成(某事)。

lot of money buying cotton, but Catherine took his arm in her two hands and spoke more violently than he had ever heard her speak before.

'You can go to New Orleans some other time. This isn't the moment to choose. We have waited too long already. '

'You said you would not be angry!' cried Morris. He got up to leave. 'Very well; we won't talk about it any more. I will do the business by letter. '

'You won't go?' said Catherine, looking at him.

Morris wanted to argue with her; it would make it easier for him to break away. 'You mustn't tell me what to do,' he said. 'Try and be calmer the next time I come. '

'When will you come again?'

'I will come next Saturday,' said Morris.

'Come tomorrow,' Catherine begged; 'I want you to come tomorrow. I will be very quiet. ' Suddenly she felt very frightened, and did not want him to leave the room.

Morris kissed the top of her head. Catherine felt her heart beat very fast. 'Will you promise to come tomorrow?'

'I said Saturday!' Morris answered, smiling. He tried to be angry at one moment, and smile at the next; it was all very difficult and unpleasant.

'Yes, Saturday, too,' she answered, trying to smile. 'But tomorrow first. ' He was going to the door, and she went with him quickly.

机会可以买棉花挣很多钱,可是凯瑟琳两手拉住他的胳膊,他从未听她说话那么激烈过。

"你可以改天再去新奥尔良,不该挑这个时候去。我们已经等得够久了。"

"你说过不会生气的!"莫里斯大声说道。他起身要走,"好吧;我们别再谈这个了。我写信来做这笔生意。"

"你不会走了?"凯瑟琳看着他说道。

莫里斯想和她吵上一架,这样分手就会容易些。"你别对我指手画脚,"他说,"下次我来的时候你冷静一点儿。"

"你什么时候再来?"

"下周六我会再来。"莫里斯说。

"明天就来吧,"凯瑟琳恳求道,"我想让你明天来。我会很安静的。"突然她感到很害怕,不想让他离开这个房间。

莫里斯吻了一下她的额头。凯瑟琳觉得心跳得很快。"答应我明天就来好吗?"

"我说了星期六!"莫里斯微笑着答道。他想要发火,但脸上立刻又挂满了笑容;这样做实在困难而且不舒服。

"是的,星期六也来,"她答道,挤出一丝笑容,"但明天先来。"他朝门口走去,她赶紧跟上他。

break away (from sb. / sth.) *escape suddenly (from captivity).* 突然逃脱;挣脱(束缚)。

'I am a busy man!' cried Morris.

His voice was so hard and unnatural that she turned away. He quickly put his hand on the door. But in a moment she was close to him again, murmuring, 'Morris, you are going to leave me.'

'Yes, for a little while. Until you are reasonable again.'

'I shall never be reasonable, in that way.' She tried to keep him longer. 'Think of what I have done!' she cried. 'Morris, I have given up everything.'

'You shall have everything back.'

'You wouldn't say that if you didn't mean something. What is it? What has happened? What have I done? What has changed you?'

'I will write to you—that is better.'

'You won't come back!' she cried, tears running down her face.

'Dear Catherine,' he said, 'don't believe that. I promise you that you shall see me again.' And he managed to get away, and to close the door behind him.

* * *

For many hours Catherine lay crying on the sofa. He had said he would return, but she had seen an expression on his face that she had never seen before. He had wanted to get away from her; he had been angry and cruel, and said strange things, with strange looks. She tried to believe that he would come back; she listened, hoping to hear his ring

"我很忙!"莫里斯大声说道。

他的声音是那么刺耳而且做作,她转过头去。他迅速把手放在了门上。可是她立刻又靠近他,低声说道:"莫里斯,你要离开我了。"

"是的,离开一阵。直到你恢复理智。"

"那样的话我永远也不会理智的。"她努力想让他多待一会儿,"想一想我所做的一切!"她哭道,"莫里斯,我放弃了一切。"

"你会重新得到那一切的。"

"要不是你有什么想法,你不会这么说的。怎么了?发生什么事了?我做了什么?是什么改变了你?"

"我会给你写信的——那样更好。"

"你不会回来了!"她哭道,泪水从脸庞上滑落。

"亲爱的凯瑟琳,"他说,"别那么想。我保证我们还会再见面的。"他挣脱了她,随手关上了门。

* * *

凯瑟琳躺在沙发上哭了好几个小时。他说过他会回来,可是她在他脸上看到了一种从未见过的表情。他已经想好了要离开她;他冲她发火,粗暴地对待她,还说一些奇怪的话,脸上的表情很陌生。她试着相信他会回来;她侧耳倾听,希望能听到他按门铃

unnatural *adj. not sincere; affected or forced.* 虚假的;做作的;勉强的。

at the door, but he did not return, nor did he call or write the next day. On Saturday Catherine sent him a note. 'I don't understand,' she wrote. 'Morris, you are killing me!'

The pain in Catherine's heart was terrible, but she was desperate to hide from her father what had happened, so she tried very hard to be brave. She ate her meals, went on with her daily life as usual, and said nothing to anybody.

'I am afraid you are in trouble, my dear,' Mrs Penniman said to her. 'Can I do anything to help you?'

'I am not in any trouble, and do not need any help,' said Catherine.

After a few days the Doctor, who had been watching in silence, spoke to his sister Lavinia.

'The thing has happened—he has left her!'

'It seems to make you happy to see your daughter upset!'

'It does,' said the Doctor; 'because it shows I was right.'

The following afternoon Catherine went for a walk, and returned to find Mrs Penniman waiting for her.

'Dear Catherine, you cannot pretend with me,' said her aunt. 'I know everything. And it is better that you should separate.'

'Separate? Who said we were going to separate?'

'Isn't it broken off?' asked Mrs Penniman.

的声音,可是他却没回头,第二天他既没来看她也没写信。星期六,凯瑟琳给他写了一张便条。"我不明白,"她写道,"莫里斯,你伤透了我的心!"

凯瑟琳内心痛苦极了,可是她却竭力不让父亲看出有什么异样,所以她努力地坚强起来。她照常吃饭,每天的生活也一如既往,对别人只字不提这件事。

"我担心你有麻烦,亲爱的,"彭尼曼夫人对她说,"我能为你做什么吗?"

"我什么麻烦都没有,也不需要任何帮助。"凯瑟琳说。

几天之后,一直在默默关注这件事的医生对姐姐拉维尼娅说:

"事情发生了——他甩了她!"

"好像你见到自己女儿难受倒挺开心的!"

"的确,"医生说,"这说明我猜得没错。"

第二天下午凯瑟琳出去散步,回来的时候发现彭尼曼夫人正在等她。

"亲爱的凯瑟琳,别瞒着我了,"她姑姑说道,"我都知道了。你们分手更好。"

"分手?谁说我们要分手?"

"不是已经解除婚约了吗?"彭尼曼夫人问道。

desperate *adj. feeling or showing great despair and ready to do anything regardless of danger.* 拼命的;不顾一切的。**break sth. off** *end sth. suddenly; discontinue sth.* 突然中止某事物;中断某事物。

'My engagement? Not at all!'

'I am sorry then. I have spoken too soon! But what has happened between you?' said Mrs Penniman; 'because something has certainly happened.'

'Nothing has happened. I love him more and more!'

Mrs Penniman was silent. 'I suppose that's why you went to see him this afternoon.'

Catherine blushed. 'Yes, I did go to see him!' she cried. 'But that's my own business!'

'Then we won't talk about it.' Mrs Penniman moved towards the door, but stopped when Catherine cried out:

'Aunt Lavinia, where has he gone? At his house they said he had left town. I asked no more questions; I was ashamed. Has he gone to New Orleans?'

Mrs Penniman had not heard of the New Orleans plan, but she did not tell Catherine this. 'If you have agreed to separate,' she said, 'the further he goes away, the better.'

Catherine stared. 'Agreed? Has he agreed it with you?'

'He has sometimes asked for my advice.'

'Is it you, then, that has changed him?' Catherine cried. 'Is it you that has taken him from me? How could you be so cruel? What have I ever done to you?'

'You are a most ungrateful girl,' said Mrs Penniman. 'It was me who helped bring you together.'

'I wish he had never come to the house! That's better

"我的婚约？根本没有！"

"那真抱歉。我这话说得太早了！可是你们俩之间发生了什么事？"彭尼曼夫人说，"因为一定有事情发生。"

"什么也没发生。我越来越爱他了！"

彭尼曼夫人沉默了："我猜你今天下午去见他就是为了这个。"

凯瑟琳脸红了。"是的，我确实去见他了！"她大声说，"可那是我自己的事！"

"那我们就别谈这个了。"彭尼曼夫人向门口走去，可听到凯瑟琳的喊声，她又止住了脚步。

"拉维尼娅姑姑，他去哪里了？他家里人说他已经走了。我不好意思再追问下去了。他去新奥尔良了吗？"

彭尼曼夫人没听说过什么新奥尔良计划，不过她没告诉凯瑟琳这个。"如果你们同意分手，"她说，"那他走得越远越好。"

凯瑟琳盯着她："同意？你们都同意这件事了？"

"他征求过我的意见。"

"那么是您改变了他的想法了？"凯瑟琳大声说道，"是您把他从我身边夺走的吗？您怎么能这么无情？我对您做过什么？"

"你真太没良心了，"彭尼曼夫人说，"是我撮合你们俩的。"

"我希望他从没来过家里！那样也比现

ashamed *adj. feeling shame, embarrassment, etc. about sth./sb. or because of one's own actions.* 感到羞耻；感到惭愧。

than this,' said poor Catherine. She was silent for a few minutes, then got up and walked around the room.

'Will you please tell me where he is?'

'I have no idea,' said Mrs Penniman.

'Will he stay away for ever?'

'Oh, for ever is a long time. Your father, perhaps, won't live for ever.'

Catherine stared at her aunt. 'He has planned it, then. He has broken it off, and given me up.'

'Only for the present, dear Catherine.'

'He has left me alone,' said Catherine, shaking her head slowly. 'I don't believe it!'

Two days later Catherine received a long letter from Morris. It explained that he was in Philadelphia, and that he would be away on business for a long time. He said he would find it impossible to forget her, but he did not want to come between her and her rightful fortune. It was his dearest wish that she should have a happy and peaceful life, and he hoped that they would one day meet as friends.

The pain that this letter gave Catherine lasted for a long time, but she was too proud to say anything about it to her aunt or her father. Doctor Sloper waited a week, before coming one morning into the back parlour, where he found his daughter alone. She was sitting with some sewing work, and he came and stood in front of her. He was going out, and had his hat on.

在这样好。"可怜的凯瑟琳说。她沉默了几分钟,然后站起身在屋里来回踱步。

"能告诉我他在哪儿吗?"

"我不知道。"彭尼曼夫人说。

"他永远也不来见我了吗?"

"噢,永远可是很长的时间。你父亲也许不会永远活着。"

凯瑟琳盯着她姑姑:"那么他早有打算了。他已经结束这段感情,放弃我了。"

"只是权宜之计,亲爱的凯瑟琳。"

"他撇下我一个人,"凯瑟琳说道,又慢慢地摇了摇头,"我不相信!"

两天后凯瑟琳收到了莫里斯的一封长信。信中说他在费城,因为有事要走很长一段时间。他还说自己对她难以忘情,可是不愿意她因为他的缘故而失去应得的财产。他最大的心愿就是她能过上幸福平静的生活,希望他们以后能像朋友一样相见。

这封信让凯瑟琳痛苦了很长一段时间,但她很爱面子,从未向姑姑或父亲提起过此事。斯洛珀医生等了一个星期,才在一天早晨来到后厅,他发现女儿独自待在那里。她坐在那里做着针线,他走过去站到她面前。他戴着帽子,正打算出门。

rightful *adj. just, proper or legal.* 正当的,正义的;合法的。

127

'I would be grateful if you would tell me when you plan to leave my house,' he said.

Catherine looked at him, with a long silent stare. 'I shall not go away!' she said.

The Doctor looked surprised. 'Has he left you?'

'I have broken off my engagement.'

'Broken it off?'

'I have asked him to leave New York, and he has gone away for a long time.'

The Doctor did not believe this, and he was disappointed at losing the chance to say that he had been right.

'How does he like your sending him away?' he asked.

'I don't know!' said Catherine.

'You mean you don't care? You are rather cruel, after playing with him for so long.'

The Doctor had his revenge, after all.

"要是你告诉我你打算什么时候离开我的家我会很感激的。"他说。

凯瑟琳默默地盯了他很久。"我不会离开的!"她说。

医生显得很惊讶:"他已经离开你了?"

"我已经退婚了。"

"退婚?"

"我让他离开纽约,他已经走了很长一段时间了。"

医生不相信这话,因为没有机会表明自己的远见卓识,他觉得有些失望。

"你让他走,他怎么想?"他问道。

"我不知道!"凯瑟琳说。

"你是说你不在乎吗? 你可真无情,跟他玩了这么久。"

医生总算尝到了报复的滋味。

have one's revenge (on sb.) (for sth.) *return an injury*. 报复;报仇。

9
Morris returns

No one ever learnt the truth about the end of Catherine's engagement. Catherine never spoke about it, keeping her secret even from Mrs Almond, who was very kind to her after Morris Townsend had left New York.

'I am delighted that Catherine did not marry him,' Mrs Almond said to her brother, 'but I wish you would be more gentle with her, Austin. Surely you feel sorry for her?'

'Why should I feel sorry for her? She has had a lucky escape. And I suspect that she has not really given him up at all. I think it is quite possible that they have made an arrangement to wait; and when I am dead, he will come back, and then she will marry him. '

Outwardly, Catherine seemed unchanged, but the fact was that she had been deeply hurt. Nothing could ever take away the pain that Morris had caused her, and nothing could ever make her feel towards her father as she had felt when she was younger.

Many years passed; years in which Catherine received more than a few offers of marriage. She refused them all, and though the name Morris Townsend was never mentioned in Washington Square, Doctor Sloper still suspected

9. 莫里斯归来

　　没有人知道凯瑟琳解除婚约的真相。凯瑟琳对此讳莫如深,连阿尔蒙德夫人都不知道她的秘密,莫里斯·汤森离开纽约后阿尔蒙德夫人对她特别好。

　　"我很高兴凯瑟琳没有嫁给他,"阿尔蒙德夫人对哥哥说,"不过我希望你对她更和善一些,奥斯汀。你一定为她感到难过吧?"

　　"我为什么要为她感到难过呢? 她运气好才没有陷进去。我怀疑她根本没有真的放弃他。我觉得很有可能他们做好了等待的安排;等我死了,他就会回来,然后她就会嫁给他。"

　　表面上看,凯瑟琳似乎没有什么变化,可实际上她受到了很深的伤害。没有什么能消除莫里斯带给她的痛苦,也没有什么能让她再像从前那样敬爱她的父亲。

　　许多年过去了;期间凯瑟琳收到过不少求婚。她统统拒绝了,虽然在华盛顿广场莫里斯·汤森的名字再也没有被提起过,斯洛

outwardly *adv. on the surface*; *apparently*. 表面上;外表上。**offer** *n. a proposal of marriage*. 求婚。

that his daughter was secretly waiting for him. 'If she is not, why doesn't she marry?' he asked himself. This idea grew stronger as he got older, and one day the Doctor said something to his daughter that surprised her very much.

'I would like you to promise me something before I die.'

'Why do you talk about dying?' she asked.

'Because I am sixty-eight years old. And I will die one day. Promise me you will never marry Morris Townsend.'

For some moments she said nothing. 'Why do you speak of him?' she asked at last.

'Because he has been in New York, and at your cousin Marian's house. Your Aunt Elizabeth tells me that he is looking for another wife—I don't know what happened to the first one. He has grown fat and bald, and he has not made his fortune.'

'Fat and bald'; these words sounded strange to Catherine. Her memory was of the most beautiful young man in the world. 'I don't think you understand,' she said. 'I almost never think of Mr Townsend. But I can't promise that.'

The Doctor was silent for a minute. 'I ask you for a particular reason. I am changing my will.'

Very few things made Catherine angry, but these words brought back painful memories from the past. She felt that her father was pushing her too far.

'I can't promise,' she simply repeated.

珀医生仍然怀疑他的女儿在秘密地等待着他。"如果她没在等,那她为什么不结婚呢?"他问自己。他越上年纪,这种想法就越强烈,结果有一天医生对女儿说了一些令她十分吃惊的话。

"我希望你在我死之前答应我一些事。"

"为什么要说起死亡来?"她问道。

"因为我已经 68 岁了,有一天我会死去。答应我你永远不会和莫里斯·汤森结婚。"

有那么半晌她什么都没说。"为什么要提起他?"她最后问。

"因为他已经回到纽约了,住在你表妹玛丽安家。你姑姑伊丽莎白跟我说他正在寻找一个新妻子——我不知道他的第一个妻子怎么了。他长胖了,头也秃了,可还是个穷光蛋。"

"又胖又秃";凯瑟琳觉得这些话听起来很陌生。她记忆中的是一个世界上最英俊的年轻人。"我想您不明白,"她说,"我几乎从没想过汤森先生。可是这件事我不能答应您。"

医生沉默了足有一分钟。"我是出于特别的原因才请求你。我要修改遗嘱。"

很少有什么事能令凯瑟琳生气,但这些话把过去的痛苦记忆又带了回来。她觉得父亲实在逼人太甚。

"我不能答应您。"她只是重复了一遍。

bald *adj.* (*of people*) *having little or no hair on the scalp.* (指人)秃头的,无发或少发的。

133

'Please explain.'

'I can't explain,' said Catherine, 'and I can't promise.'

A year later Doctor Sloper died after a three-week illness. The will he had changed shortly before his death now left Catherine only a fifth of his property. Mrs Penniman thought that this was cruel and unjust, but Catherine was neither surprised nor unhappy about the new will. 'I like it very much,' she told her aunt.

* * *

Catherine and Mrs Penniman continued to live in the house in Washington Square. On a warm evening in July, a year after Doctor Sloper's death, the two ladies sat together at an open window, looking out on the quiet square.

'Catherine,' said Mrs Penniman. 'I have something to say that will surprise you. I have seen Morris Townsend.'

Catherine remained very still for some moments. 'I hope he was well,' she said at last.

'I don't know. He would like very much to see you.'

'I would rather not see him,' said Catherine, quickly.

'I was afraid you would say that,' said Mrs Penniman. 'I met him at Marian's house, and they are so afraid you will meet him there. I think that's why he goes. He very much wants to see you.' Catherine did not answer, and Mrs Penniman went on. 'He is still very handsome, though of course he looks older now. I believe he married some lady somewhere in Europe. She died soon

"请你解释。"

"我不能解释,"凯瑟琳说,"我也不能答应。"

一年后,斯洛珀医生被病痛折磨了三个星期之后去世了。去世前不久他更改了遗嘱,只给凯瑟琳留下了五分之一的财产。彭尼曼夫人觉得这太绝情,而且不公平,但是凯瑟琳对于新遗嘱既没有感到惊讶也没有感到不高兴。"我很喜欢它。"她告诉她姑姑。

* * *

凯瑟琳和彭尼曼夫人仍然住在华盛顿广场的房子里。七月的一个温暖的晚上,此时斯洛珀医生过世已有一年之久,这两位女士一起坐在打开的窗户前,望着外面宁静的广场。

"凯瑟琳,"彭尼曼夫人说,"我有些话要对你讲,一定会让你感到惊喜。我见到莫里斯·汤森了。"

凯瑟琳一动不动地待了一会儿。"我希望他过得还好。"她最后说。

"我不知道。他很想见你。"

"我倒宁愿不见他。"凯瑟琳很快地说道。

"我料到你就会那么说。"彭尼曼夫人说道,"我在玛丽安家里遇见了他,而他们非常担心你会在那里碰到他。我想那正是他去那里的原因。他很想见你。"凯瑟琳没有回答,于是彭尼曼夫人又继续说:"他还是很英俊,虽然他现在看起来当然是老了一些。我想他是在欧洲的什么地方和某个女人结了婚。

remain v. continue to be; stay in the same condition. 仍然是;保持不变。

135

after-wards—as he said to me, she only passed through his life. The first thing he did was to ask me about you. He had heard you had never married; he seemed very much interested about that. He said you had been the real romance in his life. '

Catherine had listened silently, staring down at the ground. At last she spoke, 'Please do not say more. '

'But he very much wants to see you. '

'Please don't, Aunt Lavinia,' said Catherine, getting up from her seat and moving quickly to the other window, where Mrs Penniman could not see that she was crying.

A week later they were again sitting in the front parlour. Catherine was working on some embroidery when Mrs Penniman suddenly said, 'Morris has sent you a message. He wishes to see you, Catherine. He is going away again, and wants to speak to you before he leaves. He says his happiness depends upon it. '

'My happiness does not,' said Catherine.

'He believes that you have never understood him, that you have never judged him rightly,' said Mrs Penniman. 'This is very painful for him, and he wants just a few minutes to explain. He wishes to meet you as a friend. '

Catherine listened without looking up from her embroidery. Then she said simply, 'Please say to Mr Townsend that I wish he would leave me alone. '

She had just finished speaking when the door bell rang.

那个女人没过多久就死了——他是这么跟我说的,她只是他生命中的过客。他首先向我问起了你。他听说你一直没有结婚;他好像对此很感兴趣。他说你是他生命中真正的爱。"

凯瑟琳默默地听着,眼睛盯着地面。最后她说:"请别再说了。"

"可他很想见你。"

"求求您别说了,拉维尼娅姑姑。"凯瑟琳说着从座位上站了起来,快步走到另一扇窗前,在那里彭尼曼夫人看不见她在哭。

一周之后她们又坐在了前厅里。凯瑟琳正在做一些刺绣的活儿,彭尼曼夫人突然说:"莫里斯给你送了个口信。他想见你,凯瑟琳。他又要走了,想在走之前和你说说话。他说他的幸福就靠这个了。"

"我的幸福可不靠这个。"凯瑟琳说。

"他相信你从来没有理解他,你也从来没有对他作出正确的判断,"彭尼曼夫人说,"这让他很痛苦,他只想用几分钟时间来解释。他希望能像朋友一样和你会面。"

凯瑟琳听着,没有从刺绣活计中抬起头。然后她只是简单地说:"请告诉汤森先生我想一个人待着。"

她话刚说完,门铃就响了。凯瑟琳抬头

embroidery *n. decoration with needlework.* 刺绣。

Catherine looked up at the clock; it was quarter past nine—
a very late hour for visitors. She turned quickly to
Mrs Penniman, who was blushing.

'Aunt Penniman,' she said, in a way that frightened her
companion, 'what have you done?'

'My dearest Catherine,' said Mrs Penniman, avoiding
her niece's eyes, 'just wait until you see him!'

Catherine had frightened her aunt, but she was also
frightened herself and before she could prevent it, the servant had opened the door and announced his name.

'Mr Morris Townsend. '

Catherine stood with her back turned to the door of the
parlour. For some moments she remained still, feeling that
he had come in. He had not spoken, however, and at last
she turned round. She saw a gentleman standing in the
middle of the room, from which her aunt had quietly left.

For a moment she did not recognize him. He was forty-
five years old, fatter, with thinning hair and a thick beard.

'I have come because—I wanted to so much,' said
Morris. It was the old voice, but it did not have the old
charm.

'I think it was wrong of you to come,' said Catherine.

'Did Mrs Penniman not give you my message?'

'She told me something, but I did not understand. '

'I wish you would let *me* tell you. '

'I don't think it is necessary,' said Catherine.

看了看表;时间是 9 点一刻——这个时候来
串门实在是太晚了。她马上转向彭尼曼夫
人,发现她的脸红了。

"彭尼曼姑姑,"她说,她说话的方式令
她的同伴感到害怕,"您做了些什么?"

"我最亲爱的凯瑟琳,"彭尼曼夫人说
道,不敢看侄女的眼睛,"等你见到他再说
吧!"

凯瑟琳把她姑姑吓了一跳,自己也吃惊
不小,她还没来得及阻止,仆人就把门打开,
报上了来客的姓名。

"莫里斯·汤森先生。"

凯瑟琳站起身来,背对着客厅门。她在
那里静静地站了一会儿,感到他进来了。然
而,他没有开口说话,最后她转过身去。她
看见一位绅士站在屋子中央,她姑姑已经悄
悄地离开了。

有那么一会儿她没认出他来。他已经
45 岁了,比以前胖了,头发稀疏,胡子浓密。

"我来是因为——我很想来。"莫里斯
说。声音还是没变,可是已经没有昔日的魅
力了。

"我认为你来是个错误。"凯瑟琳说。

"彭尼曼夫人没告诉你我的口信吗?"

"她跟我说了一些事,可是我不明白。"

"我希望你能让我来告诉你。"

"我觉得没必要。"凯瑟琳说。

charm n. *power of pleasing, fascinating or attracting people; attractiveness.* 迷人或吸引人的
力量;魅力。

139

'Not for you, perhaps, but for me. ' He seemed to be coming nearer; Catherine turned away. 'Can we not be friends again?' he asked.

'We are not enemies,' said Catherine.

He moved close to her; she saw his beard, and the eyes above it, looking strange and hard. It was very different from his old—from his young—face. 'Catherine,' he murmured, 'I have never stopped thinking of you. '

'Please don't say these things,' she answered.

He looked at her again silently. 'It hurts you to see me here. I will go away; but you must allow me to come again. '

'Please don't come again,' she said. 'It is wrong of you. There is no reason for it. You behaved badly towards me. '

'That is not true,' cried Morris. 'You had your quiet life with your father—I did not want to steal it from you. '

'Yes; I had that. '

Morris could not say that she also had some of her father's property; though he knew about Doctor Sloper's will. 'Catherine, have you never forgiven me?'

'I forgave you years ago, but we cannot be friends. '

'We can if we forget the past. We still have a future. '

'I can't forget — I don't forget,' said Catherine. 'You behaved too badly. I felt it very much; I felt it for years. I can't begin again—everything is dead and buried. I never expected to see you here again. '

"对你来说也许没必要,可是对我来说有必要。"他好像走得更近了;凯瑟琳转过身去。"我们难道不能再作朋友吗?"他问道。

"我们并不是敌人。"凯瑟琳说。

他走近她;她看到了他的胡须,还有上面的那双眼睛,看起来陌生而冷峻。这和他从前的——他年轻时的——面容非常不同。"凯瑟琳,"他低声说道,"我一直在想念你。"

"请别说这些话。"她答道。

他又默默地看了看她:"在这里见我让你难过。我会走的;不过你一定要允许我再来。"

"请不要再来了,"她说,"这样不好。没理由这么做。你对我太差劲了。"

"不是这样的,"莫里斯叫道,"你和你父亲在一起平静地生活——我不想把这种生活从你身边偷走。"

"是啊;我有过这样的生活。"

莫里斯不能说她还有一些她父亲的财产;尽管他知道斯洛珀医生遗嘱的事情。"凯瑟琳,你从来没有原谅过我吗?"

"我多年以前就原谅你了,但我们不能作朋友。"

"如果忘记过去我们就能作朋友。我们还有未来。"

"我忘不掉——我不会忘记,"凯瑟琳说,"你的表现很差劲。我深有体会;我体会了很多年。我不能从头再来——一切都成了过眼云烟。我从没想过会在这里再次见到你。"

bury *v. dismiss* (*sth.*) *from one's mind; completely forget about.* 从记忆中除去(某事物);忘记。

Morris stood looking at her. 'Why have you never married?' he asked, suddenly.

'I didn't wish to marry.'

'Yes, you are rich, you are free. Marriage had nothing to offer you.' He looked around the room for a moment. 'Well, I had hoped that we could still be friends.'

'There is no possibility of that,' said Catherine.

'Goodbye, then,' said Morris.

He bowed, and she turned away. She stood there, looking at the ground, for some moments after she had heard him close the door of the room.

In the hall he found Mrs Penniman.

'Your plan did not work!' said Morris, putting on his hat.

'Is she so hard?' asked Mrs Penniman.

'She doesn't care a button for me,' said Morris. He stood for a moment, with his hat on. 'But why, then, has she never married?'

'Yes—why?' said Mrs Penniman. 'But you will not give up—you will come back?'

'Come back! Certainly not!' And Morris Townsend walked out of the house, leaving Mrs Penniman staring.

Catherine, meanwhile, in the parlour, picking up her embroidery, had seated herself with it again—for life.

莫里斯站在那里看着她。"为什么你一直没结婚?"他突然问道。

"我不想结婚。"

"是啊,你有钱,你很自由。婚姻不能给你带来什么。"他环顾了一下房间,"嗯,我本希望我们还可以作朋友。"

"那不可能。"凯瑟琳说。

"那么,再见。"莫里斯说。

他鞠了一躬,她却转过身去。听到他把房门关上之后好一会儿,她还站在那里,望着地面。

他在大厅里见到了彭尼曼夫人。

"你的计划没用!"莫里斯说着戴上了帽子。

"她的心这么硬?"彭尼曼夫人问道。

"她一点儿也不在乎我,"莫里斯说。他站了一会儿,帽子戴在头上,"可是,那她为什么不结婚?"

"是啊——为什么?"彭尼曼夫人说,"不过你不会放弃——你还会回来吧?"

"回来! 当然不会!"莫里斯·汤森走出房子,留下彭尼曼夫人在那里发愣。

与此同时,在客厅里,凯瑟琳捡起刺绣,坐在那里继续做活儿——为了生活。

bow *v. bend the head or body as a sign of respect or as a greeting.* 鞠躬;点头(表示尊敬或打招呼)。

ACTIVITIES

Before Reading

1. **Read the story introduction of the book. Match the adjectives with the people.**

   Catherine Sloper   *Mrs Penniman*
   Dr Austin Sloper   *Morris Townsend*

   amusing, charming, clever, dull, foolish, gentle, handsome, interesting, quiet, rich, simple

2. **What is going to happen in the story? Can you guess? For each sentence, choose the best word(s) to complete it.**

   1) Mrs Penniman *will / won't* be very friendly with Morris Townsend.
   2) Catherine's father will say that Catherine *can / cannot* marry Morris Townsend.
   3) Catherine will *agree / refuse* to marry Morris Townsend and later *refuse / agree*.
   4) Catherine will *please / disappoint* her father in the end.
   5) Dr Sloper will die and Catherine will inherit *all / some / none* of his money.
   6) Catherine *will / won't* marry Morris Townsend and will be *happy / miserable*.

ACTIVITIES

While Reading

1. Read Chapter 1, and then answer these questions.

1) Why was Dr Sloper successful?

2) Why was Dr Sloper lucky?

3) What happened to Dr Sloper's son?

4) What happened to Dr Sloper's wife?

5) Who came to live with Dr Sloper when Catherine was ten?

6) What did Dr Sloper want Catherine to become?

7) How did he feel about Catherine?

8) How did Catherine feel about her father?

9) Why was Catherine going to be rich?

10) Where did Dr Sloper move to in 1835?

2. Read Chapters 2 and 3. Are these sentences true (T) or false (F)? Rewrite the false ones with the correct information.

1) Morris Townsend was a cousin of Marian Almond.

2) Catherine talked a lot to Morris Townsend.

3) Mrs Penniman liked Morris Townsend.

4) Morris Townsend was working in an office.

5) Morris Townsend wanted to court Catherine.

6) Several young men had come courting Catherine before.

7) Morris Townsend had spent all his money amusing himself.

145

8) Dr Sloper didn't like Morris Townsend because he was poor.

3. Read Chapters 4 and 5. Who said this, and to whom? Who or what were they talking about?

1) 'What is going on in this house?'

2) 'But he has paid for it. '

3) 'Perhaps I should give him another chance. '

4) 'You advise me, then, not to give up hope?'

5) 'I am their teacher. '

6) 'We must do our duty; we must speak to my father. '

7) 'You have gone very fast. '

8) 'I accept that she will think I am cruel for a year. '

9) 'I am very sorry for Catherine. '

10) 'Don't let her marry him. '

4. Before you read Chapters 6 and 7, can you guess what will happen? Circle Y (Yes) or N (No) for each sentence.

1) Dr Sloper tells Catherine about Mrs Montgomery and she decides not to marry Morris. Y / N

2) Mrs Penniman helps Catherine to forget Morris. Y / N

3) Dr Sloper tells Catherine that she won't get his money if she marries Morris Townsend. Y / N

4) With her aunt's help, Catherine marries Morris secretly. Y / N

5) Catherine and Morris decide to wait before getting married. Y / N

6) Dr Sloper is amused by Catherine's situation. Y / N

7) Dr Sloper takes Catherine away to Europe. Y / N

8) Morris Townsend goes away to Europe. Y / N

5. Read Chapter 8. Choose the best question-word for these questions and then answer them.

What / Who / Why

1) ... thought that Morris would make Catherine a bad husband?

2) ... did Catherine expect from her father?

3) ... did Catherine make Morris promise?

4) ... did Morris decide to give Catherine up?

5) ... wanted Catherine and Morris to have a last parting?

6) ... did Catherine think that Morris would not come back?

7) ... reason did Morris give in his letter for leaving Catherine?

8) ... did Catherine feel when she got Morris's letter?

9) ... did Catherine tell her father about her engagement?

6. Before you read Chapter 9 (*Morris returns*), can you guess what happens? Circle Y (Yes) or N (No) for each of these sentences.

1) Everyone finds out the truth about Catherine's broken engagement. Y / N

2) Several other men ask Catherine to marry them. Y / N

3) Catherine promises her father that she will never

marry Morris Townsend. Y / N
4) Dr Sloper changes his will before he dies, and does not leave Catherine all his money. Y / N
5) After Dr Sloper's death, Morris Townsend comes back and Catherine marries him. Y / N

ACTIVITIES

After Reading

1. **Whose thoughts are these? Who are they thinking about and when? Then find words in the story which mean the opposite of the words in italic.**

   1) 'I don't want to marry her if her father disinherits her. She's very *dull*, and I must have money—I'm tired of being *poor*. But that last meeting was so *difficult* and *unpleasant*. I won't go back again—I'll write her a letter instead . . . '

   2) 'It was very *foolish* of Lavinia to be so *friendly* with him—and now look what's happened. He's gone away and the poor girl is so *miserable*. I must be *kind* to her. '

   3) 'He's so *handsome* and *self-confident*. I don't know why my cousin said he was *conceited*—I thought he was very *sincere* and natural. I *admired* him very much. My aunt *liked* him too, and she thought that he was very *clever* . . . '

   4) 'I never thought that she would *amuse* me so much. But she's too *soft* and *weak* to fight her own battles, and he's not a suitable husband for her. He's *selfish* and *lazy*—and his sister has just told me that I am *right*. '

   5) 'He seemed *annoyed* with me today. I know I

149

advised a secret marriage last week, but that was before Austin spoke to me so *coldly*. Young people are never *grateful* ... '

2. **Complete the conversation that Mrs Penniman had with Morris Townsend at Marian Almond's party. Use as many words as you like.**

MRS PENNIMAN: So you are a cousin of Arthur Townsend. Why haven't we seen you here in New York before?

MORRIS: _____.

MRS PENNIMAN: How interesting! I have never travelled much myself. And why have you returned to New York?

MORRIS: _____.

MRS PENNIMAN: So are you living with your parents?

MORRIS: _____.

MRS PENNIMAN: I'm sure that makes your sister very happy. I expect you help her with the children?

MORRIS: _____.

MRS PENNIMAN: Oh, like me! I have lived with Catherine since she was ten years old, and have been a teacher to her.

MORRIS: _____?

MRS PENNIMAN: Yes, she died when Catherine was a baby. But I have tried to be a mother to her. She's looking very fine tonight, don't you think?

150

MORRIS: _____.

MRS PENNIMAN: Yes, it *is* a beautiful dress—very expensive, of course.

MORRIS: _____?

MRS PENNIMAN: Oh no, money's not a problem. Catherine will inherit a large fortune from her father, you know.

3. Complete the letter that Morris wrote to Catherine after he went to Philadelphia. Choose the best word for each gap.

Dear Catherine

I am _____ to you from Philadelphia. _____ am afraid that I _____ going to be away _____ a long time on _____ business. I will never _____ you, but I couldn't _____ myself if you lost _____ your money because of _____. It is better for _____ to separate than to _____ each other unhappy. Please _____ that I am only _____ of you. My dearest _____ is for you to _____ a happy and peaceful _____. This will not be _____ if we marry. You _____ your father and want _____ please him, but he _____ be very angry and _____ his will if you _____ not obey him. You _____ marry a man that _____ father likes, or give _____ your property and be _____. So I have gone _____, because I do not _____ to injure you. I _____ when I come back, _____ will be able to _____ as friends.

Morris

151

4. **Imagine that the story had a different ending. Choose one of these possibilities and use the notes to write about what happened. Finish the story with your own ideas.**

   1) Catherine not go to Europe / marry Morris secretly / Dr Sloper never forgive her / no money / ...

   2) Catherine come back from Europe / marry Morris / Dr Sloper forgive her / Catherine inherit fortune / ...

5. **Do you agree (A) or disagree (D) with these statements? Explain why.**

   1) Dr Sloper: 'You are good for nothing unless you are clever.'

   2) Mrs Penniman: 'My dear Austin, you are making a great mistake if you think that Catherine is a weak woman.'

   3) Mrs Almond (about Morris Townsend): 'He will make Catherine a bad husband.'

   4) Catherine (about her father): 'And I think he despises me ... Of course it isn't my fault, but neither is it his fault.'

   5) Morris Townsend (to Catherine): 'Yes, you are rich, you are free. Marriage had nothing to offer you.'

6. **Do you think that *Washington Square* is a good title for this story? Would you prefer one of these titles instead? Why?**

   Rich Man's Daughter   A Cruel Father   Catherine

Waiting for Morris   A Foolish Girl   A Dollar Romance

7. **Which of these qualities are important when you decide to marry someone? Put them in order (1 for the most important). Explain why. Add any other ideas of your own.**

It is important to marry someone ...

- who has a lot of money.
- that your parents choose for you.
- with the same interests as you.
- that your parents like.
- who is handsome / pretty.

- that you love.
- who loves you.
- who is clever.
- who is good.
- that you like.